MEDITATE REJUVENATE

by

PAUL GALBRAITH

MEDIA MASTERS
SINGAPORE

Meditate Rejuvenate

Copyright © 1997 by Paul Galbraith
and Media Masters Pte Ltd

Published by:
Media Masters Pte Ltd
Newton Road PO Box 272
Singapore 912210
Fax: (65) 484 2559

Editing, lay-out, design
& illustrations by Media Masters
Printed by C.O.S. Printers Pte Ltd, Singapore

First published September 1997
1st reprint October 1997

Distributed exclusively throughout the United Kingdom by
John Wilson Booksales, 1 High Street, Princes Risborough,
Bucks HP 27 OAG.
Telephone (1844) 275927, Fax (1844) 274402.

ISBN 981-00-8126-X

Also by the same author:
Reversing Ageing — the Natural Way;
The Double Fat Burning Exercise Program

PREFACE

What would you give for a relatively stress-free life, for better health and happiness?

Fifteen minutes, twice a day, is all I ask of your busy lives. All you need are a quiet spot and the will to take that much needed pause. No fancy clothes, no driving to the gym, no club dues to pay.

MEDITATE REJUVENATE. The title of this book is two-pronged.

When you meditate, rejuvenation necessarily follows. One simply leads to the other. It is the horse and carriage situation here.

Meditate Rejuvenate also has the calming effect of a mantra. Rejuvenation spawned by a higher consciousness leads to a mature acceptance of a varied vista of the world. Rejuvenated, you work towards your goals and celebrate your victories. Rejuvenated, you also accept, with calmness and good humour, the fact that there are things that may not go your way. You remember that, anywhere, at home or at work, with friends or family, it is pointless to put a lid on trouble or unhappiness — a stressful exercise.

A rejuvenated mind views problems as challenges that sharpen one's mettle. It knows that serenity, happiness, delight and laughter are options. They are choices within one's reach.

When I was working on my first book, *Reversing Ageing — the Natural Way,* I discovered, to my amazement, that over and above youthful looks, flat stomachs and toned muscles, people wanted "stress-release". The people I spoke to in the course of my research all wanted "peace of mind".

This meditation book has been planned primarily to answer the stress-reduction requirement. There are two layers of stress that can be meditated out of our lives. There is the acute but superficial layer caused by daily irritants such as traffic jams and queues in banks and supermarkets, noisy neighbours and the constant ringing of telephones. Then there is the chronic and deeper layer of calcified grudges, the unresolved resentments and regrets.

A few meditation sessions will take care of the first layer. You will notice a difference in your life immediately. Then, as you meditate more, the deeper layer of chronic stress will gradually dissolve.

The cumulative effect of meditation cannot be overemphasised. We may primarily meditate to release stress but we will, at the same time, be reaping other benefits. As the two layers of stress thin out, we become more in touch with ourselves, more centred, more positive and more confident. A higher consciousness manifests itself, giving way to clearer minds, more creative perspectives and finer feelings. These are the by-products of meditation.

Without doubt, the most rewarding side-effect of meditation is that it makes us happy. The expulsion of chronic stress, the coming to terms with the various aspects of living and the raising of the level of our consciousness make us happy with and in ourselves.

I have been meditating for many years. I have studied, experimented on and compared countless techniques. I have examined their results.

The meditation techniques I recommend in this book are the most effective ones. They are natural, effortless and enjoyable.

Most of our problems stem from impatience. We want the things we desire to be ours right away. We simply cannot wait, are unwilling to wait. We overextend ourselves, then we wonder why we are stressed out and unhappy.

Likewise, we want to be relaxed and enlightened, right now. I suggest you read the book slowly and take in the notes, chapter by chapter. If you skip parts and, in your impatience, meditate straightaway, without proper preparation, the benefits will be limited. There are preliminary exercises that will maximise the results of your meditation sessions. I have organised this book in such a way that by the time you reach Chapter 7 — *Your Meditation Sessions* — you are truly prepared for them.

Think of the fifteen-minute twice daily sessions as the most important investment of your life. There are no risks involved; there are untold profits to gain.

PAUL GALBRAITH

CONTENTS

CHAPTER 1

Understanding Stress

**The goal is certainly not to avoid stress —
there is no more justification for avoiding
stress than there is for shunning food,
exercise, or love.**

Dr. Hans Selye

Ageing, according to Sir Hans Selye, founder of the International Institute of Stress, is nothing more than the sum total of all the scars and tensions of life. These scars are, in the medical sense, not only lines in your skin; they can be chemical and mental, and do irreparable damage.

In *The Stress of Life*, a trailblazing study published nearly forty years ago, the professor examined the great danger internal stress poses. It is, he said, more damaging than anything we confront in our environment.

Unresolved resentments, bottled-up anger and festering grudges don't just make us vulnerable; they make us frail, physically. Our bodies' immunity is lowered and we constantly feel unwell. Then the colds, the fevers, the ulcers and the hypertension come.

Let us review what stress does to us.

You've certainly heard people talk about getting up on the wrong side of the bed. This is supposed to explain away their short tempers, grouchiness and an over-all ill-humour during the day.

Given a chance, anyone who gets up on the wrong side of the bed will tell those willing to listen:

- *I had a disturbed sleep, in fact, I hardly slept at all!*
- *After seven or eight hours of turning and tossing in bed, I felt tired and simply couldn't get going.*
- *My neck pains and my shoulder pains didn't make it any easier.*
- *Don't ask me to concentrate ("My focus is shot to pieces!");*
- *Considering the above, I'd rather go back to bed and forget it all.*

But hardly anyone gets the luxury of going back to bed and forgetting it all. Not possible. Out there lurking are factors that can distract, annoy or threaten. These are called *stressors*. The list is endless. There is the meeting in half an hour. There's the ringing of the phone. A salesman is leaning on the doorbell. A child has to be fetched from ballet lessons. The report is four days overdue. A cheque has bounced. The dog is sick.

OH GAWD! I'm late, I'm late, I'm very, very late!

Will tomorrow be any better?

Perhaps not. Today's worries usually filter into one's evening and keep one awake until the little hours of morning. Chances are, tomorrow will simply be a repeat of today's agony.

For large numbers of people, life is a series of unimaginative, sluggish and tiring days. As each day passes, the little niggling problems get magnified. The traffic snarl gets more and more unbearable. The telephonist sounds ruder by the hour. One's spouse appears increasingly thoughtless. The world just gets less tolerable by the minute.

The mind resents all that. It gets restless; it protests: Something must be done!

Something must be done before we ourselves become stressors to the lives of the people around us. A grouch is pretty heavy company. Who wants to have a litany of complaints recited as dessert is served? Would you like to spend a weekend with someone who thinks the world stinks?

UNDERSTANDING STRESS MAKES IT LESS AWESOME

One resolves not to get up on the wrong side of the bed. A good idea. But how does one rise to greet another day when the mind has wrestled with a jumble of thoughts during the night?

There are no two ways about it: Stress should be kept at a manageable level for us to lead reasonably healthy and happy existences.

It is important for us to examine the nature of stress. Understanding it makes it less awesome and, therefore, easier to combat.

A good non-technical definition of stress which very well serves the purpose of this book is this: **STRESS IS THE PERCEPTION THAT CIRCUMSTANCES HAVE EXCEEDED ONE'S ABILITY TO COPE.**

The operative word is **perception**. We often assume that stress is a force external to us; we identify it with the disagreeable situation we confront. We then make the basic mistake of directing our attention to this external force. The fact is, the stress we feel occurs *in us*. It is our response to a stressor. Our attention therefore should be directed *inwards*.

A healthy dose of challenge is needed to make life less than humdrum. Boredom is, in itself, trying. A drab lifestyle triggers unhealthy psychological stress. The psychiatrist Robert Seidenberg refers to it as "the trauma of eventlessness," suffered by people with very stable lives devoid of challenge. Vicarious thrills gathered from pulp fiction and horror movies tend to aggravate the situation. Do we need stress? In limited, manageable doses, it can make life brighter. This is the reason why we get around to planning long haul trips, setting up exercise regimens, plotting career goals and mapping out various personal projects. We want to say, "Well, that's another thing done!"

It's all very well if nothing interrupts us. But, the fact of the matter is, life is crammed with interruptions. It wouldn't be life if the important phone call you were expecting all morning came AFTER you had stepped from the shower. Nor would it be life if your husband unexpectedly landed home with six hungry guests the very day you re-stocked the refrigerator with a week's rations. Life IS when you miss the call because you fail to hear the telephone over the noise of the shower and when the unheralded arrival of guests finds you with an empty refrigerator.

The quality of our response to such interruptions is vital.

What is the common reaction to interruptions and other stressful situations? Do we minimise their effect? Seldom. We tend to confirm, through them, perceived realities. Important calls always come at the wrong time. Uninvited guests inevitably arrive when you are least prepared. Examinations are frightening. Children are messy. Traffic jams are horrid. Taxes are dreadful.

We recognise these observations as hard and fast rules. We frequently magnify their impact.

STRESS IS NOT A NEW PHENOMENON

Our age did not invent stress. In the 1880s, the American physician George Beard wrote about the stresses of modern life. He described their effects as "nervous exhaustion".

The good old days were not devoid of problems. People had to contend with unnamed diseases for which cure appeared impossible. There was famine. There were wars.

Every age has its own set of worries. Ours is obsessed with careers, material acquisitions and technological advancement.

The man who initiated stress research, Dr Hans Selye, wrote: "The goal is certainly not to avoid stress — there is no more justification for avoiding stress than there is for shunning food, exercise, or love."

Dr Selye viewed stress as "the non-specific response of the body to any demand made upon it." Proceeding from this premise, everything, from having to answer the telephone to the foreclosure of a mortgage, spells stress. This all-embracing definition makes stress synonymous to life!

Since it appears there can be no total escape from stress in this world, it is imperative that we learn to adapt intelligently to the various demands, big and small, that get heaped on us.

INSTINCTIVE RESPONSES

Our bodies are designed to deal with sudden danger; they are made for brief responses. They function best in basic survival of the fittest situations where stress is faced and contained in minutes. Adrenaline is released into the bloodstream and we respond immediately to a perceived harm. If we save a child or a pet from getting run over by a car, the sudden jolt to our nerves

can leave us on a mental high. We were momentarily stressed but we've come out on top. End of story.

WHY WE CANNOT COPE WITH THE STRESSES OF MODERN LIFE

"Nature" actually designed stress for a purpose. In "pre-civilisation" times, acute stress served a very important function. It prepared the body to fight or escape from wild animals or enemies. To prepare for this, a multitude of physiological changes occurred in the body. These are collectively known as the **"Fight or flight response"**. Examples of some of these changes are:

- Our muscles begin to contract, thereby fortifying our 'body armour'. We are now more protected from bodily injury.

- Our metabolism speeds up, providing more strength and energy with which to fight or run. The heart rate and the amount of blood pumped with each beat increase.

- Our rate of breathing begins to increase, providing more oxygen to the brain and muscles.

- Our digestive system begins to shut down, diverting more blood and energy to the large muscles needed to fight or run.

- Arteries to our arms and legs begin to constrict. Our blood begins to clot more quickly. Thus, less blood would be lost if we were wounded or injured.

In the old days, stress was mainly physical, and therefore the response was physical: fight or flight. After a physical challenge, the body relaxed and the person was probably all the better for the incident.

We are not made to be strung-out. That, by and large, is the cause of our unhappiness. Still, most of us have lifestyles involving chronic problems and protracted battles for survival. There are financial worries, relationship puzzles, professional dilemmas. We now confront situations where the body is unable to relax because of on-going stress. The adrenaline released into the bloodstream is made to stretch to cope with 15-year mortgages or the incessant ups and downs of a thankless job. We spend sleepless nights longing for a new car. We ache to upgrade our accommodations. We sulk because we cannot spend our birthday in some expensive holiday resort.

Today, a lot of stress is caused by wants rather than needs. No longer beset with problems of physical survival, we have turned our attention to and are consumed by lists often dictated by greed and envy. Keeping Up With The Neighbours is our age's version of the plague.

We cope, and coping is stressful.

The beneficial acute stress that serves fight or flight responses becomes chronic. We maintain muscle tension, high blood pressure and an excessive mental alertness we commonly refer to as anxiety. The same responses that are designed to protect us become harmful, even lethal. Arteries constrict, not just in our arms and legs but also inside our hearts. Blood clots are more likely to form inside our coronary arteries.

STRESS OVERLOAD

The following are common symptoms of stress overload:

- Over-reacting (extreme impatience or excessive anger) to minor problems;

- Increased consumption of alcohol, cigarettes or tobacco;

- Overeating or loss of appetite;

- Disturbed sleep;

- Reduced work efficiency and decision-making ability;

- Psychosomatic disorders manifested in physical symptoms like headaches, neck tension, heart palpitations and skin disorders.

People respond physically to stress in many ways. Initially, stress produces a response in the body which prepares it for action. This response boosts the running level of the body to enable it to cope with increased demand on the system. You may be able to picture this higher running level if you think of the response you get when you step on the accelerator of a car while it is in neutral. If the stress response is prolonged, this higher running level leads to physical damage and exhaustion. Almost every part of the body is affected.

Immediate physical responses include increased heart, perspiration and breathing rates, muscle tension and dry mouth.

The increased mental anguish brings about internal changes which include a rise in blood pressure, an increase in blood fats, sugar and cholesterol, a decreased immune response resulting in an increased susceptibility to viruses, colds, etc. and an increased tendency of the blood to clot.

Longer term physical responses may include stress-related health problems such as back pain, rashes, stomach upsets, insomnia, peptic ulcer, heart disease, high blood pressure and chronic fatigue.

"COLD OF THE MIND"

Stress and the accompanying negative feelings of anxiety and depression are often referred to as the "common cold of the mind." Large numbers of the general population complain of tiredness upon waking up, of feeling out of sorts, of just "not being there."

One major study conducted in the United States showed that men and women reacted differently to stress. Men tended to suffer more from physical ailments such as heart disease and ulcers while women suffered more from emotional problems such as anxiety and depression. At the same time, both men and women showed similar reactions to stress overload such as working excessively or settling for the quick fixes, like alcohol or tranquillisers.

WARNING SIGNALS & NATURE'S PURPOSE

Like pain, stress is nature's way of telling us that something is amiss in our lives. It's like a red light that flickers on the instrument panel of cars, alerting us to a malfunctioning of our vehicles.

To ignore nature's warning is to thwart nature's purpose and the result can only be adverse. Chronic stress results in serious

JOB STRESS

The rating is on a scale from 0 to 10. The higher the rating the greater the stress.

Miner	8.3	Diplomat	4.8
Policeman/woman	7.7	Farmer	4.7
Airline pilot	7.5	Vet	4.4
Building worker	7.5	Civil Servant	4.3
Journalist	7.5	Accountant	4.3
Prison Officer	7.5	Engineer	4.3
Advertising executive	7.3	Estate Agent	4.3
Dentist	7.3	Hairdresser	4.3
Actor	7.2	Secretary	4.3
Politician	7.0	Solicitor	4.3
Doctor	6.8	Artist/Designer	4.0
Taxman	6.8	Architect	4.0
Film producer	6.5	Chiropodist	4.0
Nurse/midwife	6.5	Optician	4.0
Fireman	6.3	Planner	4.0
Pop musician	6.3	Postman	4.0
Teacher	6.2	Statistician	3.8
Personnel Officer	6.0	Lab Technician	3.7
Social worker	6.0	Banker	3.7
Manager	5.8	Computer operator	3.7
Press officer	5.8	Linguist	3.7
Professional footballer	5.8	Occupational Therapist	3.5
Salesman/assistant	5.7	Beauty therapist	3.5
Stockbroker	5.5	Astronomer	3.3
Bus driver	5.4	Nursery nurse	2.8
Psychologist	5.2	Museum worker	2.0
Publisher	5.0		

health disorders; it could lead to nervous breakdowns. The damage done by everyday minor hassles is cumulative. Office politics, daily traffic snarls, and chaotic schedules do add up and put a severe strain on the nerves.

TRYING EVENTS

In the 1960s, Thomas Holmes, M.D., a psychiatrist and Richard Rahe, a psychologist, undertook a major study to measure the amount of stress individual situations produce. What they found was that people who had the **most changes** in their lives — either positive or negative — **suffered the most illnesses**.

They devised a 100-point scale rating 43 life events (later revised to 63) by the degree of stress each produced. This is what they found.

- death of a spouse .... 100 points

- divorce .... 73 points

- marital separation .... 65 points

- prison sentence .... 52 points

- injury or illness .... 52 points

- buying a house .... 51 points

- marriage .... 50 points

- applying for a loan .... 17 points

- holiday .... 12 points

- getting booked for a traffic offence .... 11 points

The Holmes - Rahe rating scale has been tested on thousands of people of all ages and nationalities and the results have proved to be consistent.

According to Holmes and Rahe, if you score between 150 and 300 points, you have a 50% chance of falling seriously ill or being involved in a serious accident within six months. If your score exceeds 300, the probability jumps to 80%.

As further evidence, one study showed that people with high blood pressure had higher levels of adrenaline, the stress hormone, than did subjects with normal blood pressure when given a word-matching test.

There is also a strong correlation between heart disease, sex problems, skin problems and stress. In a Swedish study, psoriasis sufferers showed higher levels of stress hormones than healthy people when subjected to stressful tests.

CHRONIC STRESS COULD BE THE CAUSE OF SPECIFIC HEALTH PROBLEMS SUCH AS:

Fast heartbeat or fast shallow breathing

This is due to a hormonal reaction of the fight or flight syndrome.

Colds

Stress may hinder the immune system. In a recent American study, scientists surveyed a range of people about the problems in their lives and then exposed them to the viruses that cause colds. It was found that those who were stressed were most likely to catch the cold viruses.

Stomach cramps/excess gas/diarrhoea/nausea

Stress causes excess secretions of acid and speeds movement through the digestive tract.

Skin and scalp problems

Stress causes hormonal or immunological changes which results in chemical changes in the skin.

Hair problems

Stress can affect the sebaceous glands which secrete oils that keep hair follicles healthy.

Neck pain

Stress can cause the neck and shoulder muscles to tighten up. This causes the muscles to release chemicals which produce muscle fatigue and pain. If this occurs over a long period, the muscles often stay tense even after the stress is removed. You may have to see a chiropractor.

Sleep problems

Stress causes both muscle tension and anxiety which put the mind in a high state of arousal. This, in turn, can result in problems with getting to sleep, waking up frequently or waking up early. Disturbances like these clearly impact on the day that follows.

Headaches and migraines

When the neck muscles tighten, it can result in a restriction of blood flow to the brain or even cause a vertebrae misalignment in the neck resulting in a "pinched nerve". Both of these can bring on headaches.

Jaw pain or grinding teeth

Stress can induce the jaw muscles to tighten resulting in pain or clicking of the jaw. Stress is also a common cause of grinding the teeth. This often occurs while you are asleep so you may not be aware you are doing it.

SAY NO TO SUPPRESSANTS

Many people attack symptoms of stress with suppressants. They drink excessively, smoke incessantly and induce rest with the aid of sleeping pills. These quick fixes can only aggravate their predicaments since alcohol, tobacco and sleeping pills are detrimental to the nervous system.

There's only one way of handling stress: **UNDERSTAND IT FOR WHAT IT IS, THEN RELEASE IT.**

HIGHLIGHTS

- Stress is mainly an internal factor and its effect depends on your attitude rather than the event itself.

- View stress as a **warning signal**. Like pain, it's nature's way of letting us know that something is wrong and we should therefore give attention to putting it right.

- Watch out for signs of stress overload.

- Stress also creates tension and conflict between people and it spoils relationships. In short it prevents us from being happy, successful and realising our full potential.

- Our in-built stress mechanisms are designed for brief and instant responses. They are counter-productive for the demands of modern life. **We need stress-release techniques.**

CHAPTER 2

BECOMING STRESS-RESISTANT

Your belief structures form the basis of
your coping mechanisms.

Can one become stress-resistant?

Two factors help minimise the harm that stress does to us. One is a positive perspective. The other is a healthy nervous system.

Stress is inherent in our daily life. There are stressors in the work place whether you are an executive with heaps of responsibility or a factory assembly wage-earner.

Social relationships can bring about tension. The "I-must-make-a-good-impression" complex has caused countless stomach upsets and migraine headaches. A whole week before dining with the Chairman of the Board, an executive wife often works herself to a point of nervous frenzy — what to wear, what to say, what flowers to bring. Then she spends the following week worrying herself sick on how well she performed: she should have worn the blue dress, she should not have talked about her children and she should have known that Mrs Chairman of the Board likes carnations.

Every now and then, our homes become seething cauldrons. These are days when our closest and dearest appear to be on a general strike. Dissent reigns and nobody is willing to budge an inch.

Children and young people are not spared. Peer pressure among teenagers causes undue anxiety. Students worry about study loads. Children have nightmares that feature classroom bullies.

DEVELOPING A HEALTHIER ATTITUDE

In his excellent book, *The Jungle is Neutral,* a study of survival in tropical hinterland, Spencer Chapman points out that the jungle takes no sides: it is neither your friend nor your foe. However, men react differently when isolated by its seeming impenetrability. There are people who find the maze of undergrowth a protective shelter and a source of nourishment; they proceed to plot routes and lay traps. But there are those who are unnerved by tangles of vines and the strange noises; they get consumed by thoughts of imminent disaster and get seized by terror.

Obviously, the people who are able to manipulate the resources about them get a better chance of survival.

Likewise, the world is neither your friend nor your enemy. YOU determine how good or bad, how happy or miserable, how full or empty your days can be. Only you can set the parameters of your comfort zones and the length of your wish list.

Your belief structures form the basis of your coping mechanisms.

The world is there for you to enjoy. Tap its resources within reason and you will not only survive, but prevail.

It will help tremendously if you approach each day without preconceived notions. Break the habit of saying, "Something in my bones tells me this day will be awful." This habit is responsible for the bone-deep, cannot-be-cured-with-vitamins-and-sleep tiredness many people complain about.

Shakespeare said, There is nothing either good or bad, but thinking makes it so. Our personal reaction to a situation can cause undue stress. The discomfort comes from within, a fact that can be remedied by a change of attitude.

As stated earlier, this does not mean you deny the reality of a stressor or a crisis. On the contrary, you recognise it immediately for what it is and then confront it accordingly.

Confronting a crisis means containing it. You accept the situation but don't let it magnify to a point where it blots out all logic and common sense.

POSITIVE ACTION

Handling stress calls for positive action. You take command. Let's say you are running late and discover you've got a flat tyre. Not your idea of an ideal morning. After the initial reaction of "Oh, no!", it's pointless to fret about life's unfairness. It's far wiser to get on the phone and tell whomever is meeting you that you will be delayed. Then change the tyre. Afterwards, sit down for a minute or two and take a few deep breaths before setting out.

Put it all behind you. The day has things to offer other than one unfortunate flat tyre.

If similar situations recur with alarming regularity, review your time management. Getting up earlier is the best solution in most cases. You may also need to look into the way you maintain your possessions.

Keeping office hours, parenting chores, money worries, frequent arguments over trifles with your partner are minor stressors. But their cumulative effect can be very damaging because there is little time between them for one to recover.

HOW DOES ONE BECOME POSITIVE?

Begin by giving proper attention to yourself. Stress is easier to manage when your vitality level is high. Life takes on a different perspective when you feel good. When stressful situations arise, you have the clarity of mind and the energy to manage them.

THE BODY–MIND CONNECTION

It is important to realise that stress is both physical and mental. The mind and body are intimately related due to the connection of all parts of the body to the brain via the nervous system. What affects the mind affects the body and vice-versa. A good illustration of this is when you exercise. Even though you are working on the physical level, you are also affecting the mind. You feel good after each session. Many joggers experience 'runners' high' — their vitality is high and at the same time they feel calm and relaxed. The physical exercise has somehow stimulated the brain to secrete endormorphins. These are the body's natural opiates and are often called the 'happy hormones'.

It also works the other way. When you sleep well, the mind is rested. This, in turn, causes the nerves and muscles to relax; again, you feel good mentally and physically. I will briefly explain how this works.

A certain degree of muscle tension is required for normal living. Even just sitting or standing requires a degree of muscle tension to support us, otherwise, gravity would cause us to collapse. This normal degree of muscle tension is determined by just the right amount of impulses travelling along the nerves to the muscles. When we are rested, as is the case after a good night's sleep, our nerve impulses are in harmony. If we don't sleep well, the nervous system is unrested and becomes overly excitable. Too many impulses are now travelling to the muscles giving messages for them to tense up. This sensation of muscle tension is relayed to the brain via different nerve lines and produces feelings of mental stress. This, in turn, causes the muscles to become even more tense and we now have **a vicious cycle** operating.

We can break this cycle by interfering at either the physical or mental level due to the intimate relationship between body and mind. Going a step further, if we co-ordinate work on both physically relaxing the muscles and mentally releasing stress, we will achieve even better results. The vicious cycle which existed will not only be broken, but will actually start working in reverse to our benefit.

THE VICIOUS CYCLE

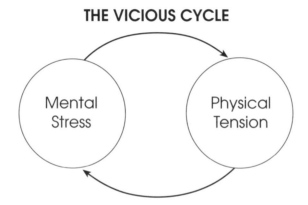

The whole basis of stress release, then, is to expel tension or anxiety mentally while physically and simultaneously relaxing the muscles.

Because we have reached a critical stage in our journey to understanding the nature of stress, I want to summarize these essential points before we go further.

• When we experience mental stress, it also causes our muscles to tense up due to the connection of the brain to the muscles via the nervous system.

• Mental stress also makes us sleep poorly, producing even more muscle tension.

• This increased muscle tension makes us feel bad and creates even more mental stress, which in turn creates even more muscle tension and so on.

• We have a vicious cycle set up which is best broken by mentally releasing stress through meditation and physically relaxing the muscles.

EXAMINING MUSCLE TENSION

In many people, the muscle tension is so chronic that a muscle relaxation technique may be necessary.

Tense muscles are really muscles whose fibres have contracted. This contraction requires energy. The energy comes from your body's energy reserves and this is why tense people usually suffer from fatigue.

To maintain this muscle tension, more impulses must travel along nerve lines to supply the muscle with the needed energy. This also uses up more of your energy bank and excessive impulses tend to produce an over-active nervous system making you feel **tense and irritable.**

Tight muscles in the spinal area are a common cause of **spinal vertebrae misalignments.** When muscles tighten up more on one side of the spine they may pull a vertebrae slightly to one side and 'pinch' a spinal nerve. Not only does this often cause **pain**, but it can also cause **other related health problems**, since the spinal nerves supply all the organs and glands of the body. For example, muscle tension or pinched nerves in the neck are a common cause of **headaches and migraines.** Since the nerves in the neck also go to the brain, **fatigue** and **poor sleep** are common added discomforts. Nerves in other areas of the spine supply the muscular walls of the blood vessels. If any of these nerves are 'pinched', the muscular walls may contract, reducing the diameter of the blood vessels and resulting in **high blood**

pressure and reduced blood flow to some of the organs and glands. This **reduces your health and vitality levels.**

Muscle contraction occurs when electrical impulses travelling down a nerve stimulates the muscle via the release of a transmitter chemical called acetyl choline. This causes the myosin filaments to slide over the actin filaments inside the muscle resulting in tension.

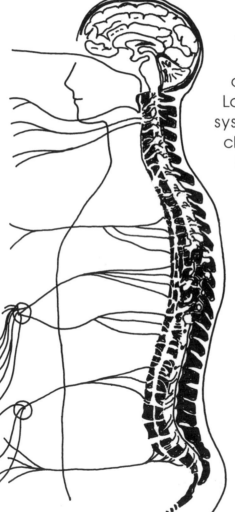

When muscles contract, a waste product of muscle metabolism is produced, called **lactic acid.** Lactic acid is a toxin to the system. If you suffer from chronic muscle tension, the lactic acid in your body may reach high levels and further reduce your health and vitality.

Muscle tension is bad news. You not only feel bad, but you will also sleep badly and your health will suffer.

There are several techniques which are very effective in relaxing the muscles and releasing muscle tension.

"PINCHED"NERVES

STRESS CAUSES REDUCED IMMUNITY

The most significant health effect of stress is to cause suppression of the body's immune system. In one study of students doing stressful examinations, antibody levels were found to be lower than normal, making them more susceptible to infection.

Researchers have also found a definite correlation between stress and vulnerability to infectious diseases such as streptococcal infections, herpes simplex and even the common cold. Stress does not cause the infection, but it reduces the body's resistance to the bacteria or viruses. Other studies have shown that aggressive Type A personalities catch more colds than the more relaxed Type B personalities.

In another US study, the immunity of women who have been divorced for one year or less was compared to married women. Researchers found blood samples of divorced women had depressed immunity.

An important part of our immune system comprises natural killer cells which seek out and destroy cancer cells. Stress represses our immune response, including our natural killer cells and this makes it easier for cancer to develop and spread to other parts of the body.

Researchers at Harvard University Medical School have verified this. They found that people who were depressed and anxious were most likely to have slow natural killer cell activity. Other studies have shown that people under stress tend to have lower blood levels of T-lymphocytes which are important for fighting infection.

RELAX THOSE MUSCLES

The following is a muscle relaxation technique. With practice, you will get very satisfying results. Ten minutes of deep relaxation will make you feel more refreshed than several hours of disturbed sleep. During normal sleep, you toss and turn and often experience mental tension from jumbled dreams. All these cause muscle tension and that's one reason why many wake up feeling tired.

In this exercise, you consciously relax your muscles and there are no unpleasant dreams to cause mental tension. It is based on an ancient yoga technique.

Try this relaxation technique in the days or weeks before you start your meditation sessions. It will make them more effective.

1. Choose a quiet place where you won't be disturbed for ten minutes or so. Take the phone off the hook or switch the answering machine on if you are alone in the house. Otherwise, make it known that you are taking a break. Your companions are not mind readers.

2. Wear loose clothes.

3. Make sure you are neither too cold nor too hot. It's best to do this exercise on the floor, with a mat underneath you, if you wish.

4. Lie flat on your back with your arms alongside your body. Make sure you feel comfortable.

5. Take slow, deep breaths. Push your abdomen forwards when inhaling then let it fall back to its normal position when exhaling. Establish this relaxed breathing pattern for a few minutes.

6. We now begin relaxing your muscles.

7. Tense your right foot and toes for about three seconds and then quickly let go. Repeat with your left foot and toes.

8. Next, tense your right leg for three seconds and then quickly let go. Repeat with your left leg.

9. Clench your right fist tightly, at the same time tensing your right arm for about three seconds. Do the same with your left fist and arm.

10. Now tense your shoulders and upper back for three seconds and let go.

11. Repeat the process with your neck, then your face, then your eyes. Just screw your face up, then let go. Close your eyes as tightly as you can, then relax.

12. Become aware of the body parts you have just relaxed. If any part still feels tense, repeat the contraction/relaxation for that part. Mentally tell the area to "let go".

13. Lie there for a few minutes, just breathing slowly and enjoying the relaxed feeling. Don't try to stop whatever thoughts arise in your mind. Just let them go, without judging them.

14. Before getting up, raise your arms above your head and stretch your whole body for a few seconds. Stretching is a very effective muscle relaxer.

15. When you stand up, shake your hands for a few seconds and then shake each foot. This releases any residual tension.

    Remember: practice makes perfect.

REGRETS AND WORRIES

Stress can be real or imagined. The imagination is powerful enough to cause discomfort by dwelling on the past (regrets) or picturing negative consequences of future events (worries).

Regrets and worries cloud our image of the world; our view is clouded by self-inflicted stress. It's like examining an object through a dirty microscope lens. The real nature of the object is obscured by the dirt on the lens.

Past conditioning, much of which was negative, has resulted in distrustful, irresponsible and spiteful people. The many don'ts of childhood haunt adults in various ways. Haven't you heard of the man who eats a biscuit before dinner whether he is hungry or not, because when he was at school, his mother would not allow him a cookie (and he begged and begged) because, she said, it would "ruin" his appetite? Then you must have met somebody who lounges

about in her bedclothes on weekends because, as a child, she had to be bathed and scrubbed first thing in the morning. A great number of TV addicts are people who had to subscribe to the dictum of "no TV on school days" when they were children.

Worriers produce anxious children. Parents who perceive the world as shark-infested usually end up with hostile off-spring. Suspicious parents and hostile children are a recipe for a stressful household.

STOP BLAMING YOUR ELDERS

Blaming your grandmother for the habits that now annoy your partner leads nowhere. Saying that you are as great a worrier as your mother will not help you get a better night's sleep.

HANDLING NEGATIVE THOUGHTS

Focus attention on yourself. A negative thought conditioning can be changed. As with breaking any habit, what we have to do is practise the opposite.

Make a habit of replacing a negative thought with a positive one. As soon as a negative picture crosses your mind, replace it with a positive image. For instance, the report you have to submit should be viewed as a challenge rather than a problem. Think of various ways you can make it interesting. As soon as you stop fretting about having to submit it and start getting involved in the actual preparation for it, your mental load is remarkably lessened.

In the beginning it will be difficult. We are, after all, dealing with a lifetime habit. Practice should make it easier until, eventually, it becomes automatic.

You will have broken one habit above any other which has been making you constantly bothered, fatigued and unhappy.

RESEARCH SHOWS THAT STRESS MANAGEMENT REDUCES COLDS/INCREASES ENERGY/BUILDS SELF ESTEEM

Research done by psychologist Barbara Hewson-Bower at Murdoch University, Western Australia, shows that stress-management techniques can increase the level of anti-bodies in saliva, making children less prone to colds and 'flu. Children recovered in three or four days instead of two weeks.

A thirteen-week study of 45 children showed that those who were taught stress-management had a total of 212 sick days, compared with 586 for those who were not. Those chosen for the study were often ill and remained sick for a long time.

The secretion of the antibody immunoglobulin A in saliva is believed to inhibit the adherence of virus and bacteria to the lining of the mouth and nose.

Children in the stress-management group also showed improvements in self esteem and energy levels and got more enjoyment from time spent with their families.

The significance of this study is, if we can teach children to control their stress levels and negative emotions, they can experience a much healthier lifestyle.

A HEALTHY NERVOUS SYSTEM HELPS

Bear in mind the importance of a healthy nervous system. This includes the brain. If we have a strong nervous system, we can handle stress with more equanimity — including even the stress produced by negative thought.

To build a strong nervous system, we have to pay attention to our lifestyle. The habits of good sleep, exercise and proper diet are fundamental.

SLEEP

Deep sleep for a long period revitalises our nervous system. When we sleep soundly, nature is able to restore and heal the body. The brain is given a rest and the body is recharged with energy.

Between seven and nine hours of sleep should be sufficient rest for adults. You must not oversleep. Oversleeping causes physical and mental sluggishness.

Sound sleep is the by-product of healthy meals and exercise. A light evening meal, without alcohol and coffee and a brisk half-hour walk before retiring are two good sleep factors.

Be sure there's good ventilation in your bedroom. The sleep centre in the brain operates better when it has fresh oxygen supply. A build-up of stale air which consists mainly of carbon dioxide in a poorly ventilated room, is another reason why many people wake up not feeling fresh.

Keep plants away from the bed area. In the evening, plants give out carbon dioxide, something you don't need.

If healthy meals, some form of aerobic exercise, good ventilation, a firm bed and a hot bath fail to deliver the deep sleep you need, a visit to a chiropractor is suggested.

A spinal misalignment could be the cause of your problem. A spinal misalignment in the neck causes pressure on the nerves and blood vessels in that area. Since these nerves and blood vessels travel to the brain, it means there is an interference to the brain's nerve and blood supply, resulting in poor sleep. Since pain is often not present, neck misalignments can cause sleep disturbance for a long, long time before it is detected and corrected.

GOOD NUTRITION

Our nervous system, like the rest of the body, needs to be well-fed. In fact, it is more important that the nervous system receives good nourishment than the rest of the body, since it controls the other eight systems.

Avoid fad diets and base your eating habits on scientific principles. Never go to extremes.

Practise the four cardinal rules of nutrition: 1) Eat slowly; 2) Give emphasis on raw food; 3) Have a balanced diet; 4) Reduce your fat and sugar intake.

Observe the two rules of optimum food combination: 1) Eat fewer different types of food at one meal and 2) Eat fruit on its own.

Cut down on salt. Eat less processed food. Use natural seasoning such as lemon juice, onions, garlic and chilli.

Have eggs and milk in moderation.

Drink when you are thirsty. Eat plenty of fruit. Fruit contains the most pure and mineral-rich water.

When you plan your food chart, think of a pyramid. The food groups that nourish your body best should make up the base. At the tip of the pyramid are items that, taken excessively, damage your health, like salt and sugar.

FOODS TO BE EMPHASISED IN THE DIET

Raw foods such as fruit, salad, bean sprouts, and raw nuts should make up about 70% of your food intake. This is not difficult to do. Have fruit for breakfast, morning and afternoon tea breaks, have a large salad and bean sprouts with one of your meals and raw nuts for dessert. The reason for this is that raw food has had **no nutrient loss** from processing and heating. In particular, the **enzymes** — the life force of foods — are preserved. Enzymes are essential for vitality and rejuvenation — even vitamins won't work without enzymes. Drink raw juices such as **carrot juice**, since most of the nutrients are in the juice and very little energy is wasted on digestion.

Fruit should comprise up to 50 percent of our diet, because it is the most nutritious food, wastes very little energy on digestion, is low in fat, eliminates toxins from the body and has healing properties.

By concentrating on raw food, you are **automatically** cutting out a lot of **fat** and **sugar** and getting more **fibre**, without any special effort.

Raw food is the **ideal food for meditation**, since foods from the vegetable kingdom have a calming effect on the mind.

FOODS TO BE EATEN MODERATELY

The foods to be eaten in moderation are grains, meat, eggs and milk.

Grains are important because they are a rich source of vitamins, but they are acidic, hard to digest and need to be cooked (that is, they are not raw). Oats (porridge, muesli) and rice are the best grains to eat. Buy wholemeal bread.

Meat should be eaten in controlled portions because it causes intestinal putrefaction, contains toxins, drugs and pesticides and can be contaminated with animal diseases. Meat is also high in fat. Replace some of your meat with fish, egg or soya bean dishes.

Milk is also best taken in moderation, since it has been processed by pasteurisation making it difficult to digest and highly mucous forming. Yoghurt is one of the better milk products, since the bacteria in it have partially digested the sugar and protein. Try to replace some of your milk with soya milk.

Eggs are highly nutritious food being rich in protein, vitamins, minerals and lecithin, but need to be eaten sparingly due to their high saturated fat levels.

FOODS TO BE DRASTICALLY REDUCED

The foods to avoid are **processed foods.** Much of their nutritional value has been destroyed by **processing and heating**; they are loaded with **harmful chemicals** and they usually contain a lot of **fat and sugar**. By processed foods we mean "fast" foods, cakes, biscuits, sweets and most canned foods. Unfortunately, much of the food on supermarket shelves is processed.

To reduce processed foods, eat more fresh fruit, vegetables and wholegrain products.

You should also **keep your sugar intake low.** Most of our sugar intake is now **hidden away in processed foods.** Just one can of soft drink contains about 10 teaspoons of sugar. **Reduce your sugar intake** by reducing processed foods, sugar added to foods and drinks, cakes and soft drinks. Replace some of your sugar with the sweet alternatives: honey, carob, fructose, molasses and dried fruit.

EXERCISE

By becoming fit, we get our body systems functioning better.

Exercise not just to lose weight but to become healthier. Ideally, exercise should increase your fitness level, improve the functioning of your organs and glands and increase the flexibility of your joints, including your spine.

Aerobics are best for cardio-vascular fitness; yoga improves the functioning of your organs and glands and increases flexibility.

When you do aerobic exercises, the duration depends on which one you do. These are the recommended times:

- Jogging .... 23 minutes

- Aerobics .... 23 minutes

- Walking .... 30 minutes

- Cycling .... 30 minutes

- Swimming .... 30 minutes

Yoga is the most effective exercise system that exists. It is almost specific for the nervous system and has potent effects on both the brain and the spine.

The reverse postures such as the headstand and the shoulder-stand greatly increase the blood supply to the brain. The increased blood and oxygen supply to the brain revitalises it as no other exercise can.

The yoga postures also stretch the spine in all directions, making it supple. At the same time, minor spinal misalignments get corrected.

GIVE YOURSELF REGULAR BREAKS

Make it a point to give yourself regular breaks from whatever task you are doing. The coffee break is a good idea, without the coffee. Use it to make your mind "breathe".

On days when you find yourself glued to a chore for hours on end, try doing the following exercises. They will impede the build-up of tension and you will therefore feel less fatigued after the job is done.

NECK EXERCISES

These exercises will also improve the flexibility of your neck.

1. Let your head drop forwards. Stay in that position for two seconds. Now let your head drop backwards. Stay in that position for two seconds. Do this exercise three times.

2. Turn your head to the right as far as you can. Now push a little further and hold it there for two seconds. Repeat this to the left. Do this three times.

3. Let your head drop sideways towards your right shoulder. Hold it there for two seconds. Repeat to the left. Do the exercise three times.

A NOTE OF CAUTION

Some books advocate the neck roll exercise, in which the neck is rolled around clockwise and then anti-clockwise. I don't recommend you do it since it jams the side joints of the neck and this can cause inflammation.

RELAX YOUR EYES

1. Close your eyes as tightly as you can. Squeeze the eyes so the eye muscles contract. Hold this contraction for three seconds, then let go quickly. This exercise relaxes the eye muscles considerably and is especially useful for those who spend hours reading or working before computer terminals.

2. Try "palming". Cup the palms of your hands over your eyes and keep your eyes gently closed. Stay in this position for one minute. You'll feel refreshed afterwards.

STRESS MANAGEMENT LOWERS BLOOD PRESSURE

According to Professor Murray Esler of Baker Medical Research Institute, Melbourne, Australia, stress management may be as effective as a low-salt diet. Esler found that meditation, yoga and programmed muscle relaxation reduces blood pressure by 5 to 7 points. There is also evidence that the effects are long lasting.

EXERCISE MODERATION

Prevention is always easier than cure. In setting goals, work within reasonable bounds. Success is wonderful but remember the ladder you have to climb — take one careful step at a time.

Try not to be tempted by indulgences you can ill afford. Financial commitments must be kept at manageable levels.

Your time is as precious as money. Don't fritter it away trying to please everybody. It's just not possible.

STOP RUSHING

What's a life spent feeling like a chicken with its head cut off? Slow down. Your work will be completed just as quickly if you take your time doing it. You will make fewer mistakes and therefore need less time to correct errors. Rushing often results in inaccuracies and omissions.

Rushing about is largely a result of nervous energy; it is largely a habit. It produces fatigue and stress.

Are you a breathless, single-minded career person obsessed with protecting your turf? Look out the window. Do you see the trees, the clouds, the vast sky? They are also important. They will be around long after you're gone.

LAUGH MORE OFTEN

Laughing is a great stress-releaser. Most of us are too serious too much of the time.

Create situations where the funny bone gets tickled. Watch funny movies; read entertaining books. Mix with people who make you laugh.

Studies show that laughing has beneficial effects on our health. This is why it is often referred to as "internal jogging".

PLAY/SOCIALISE

All work and no play indeed makes Jack and Jill dull, dull people. Don't view leisure as a waste of time. Recreation means, literally, to re-create. You will be far more productive if you take time off from a project and allow yourself sufficient time to recharge your batteries.

Every now and then, see people. Talk to them, eat with them. It's better if these people are not office-mates or neighbours. You don't want to end up discussing departmental intrigues or some petty neighbourhood gossip that may unnecessarily bother you.

Cultivate social relationships where you discuss things outside your immediate suburban interests. There exist people other than your supervisor, your children and your erring mate. Form opinions and learn to defend them. Friendly debates about governments, sports, books and even TV shows are stress-releasers.

SAY NO TO QUICK FIXES

We've said this earlier and we are saying it again here because it is *that* important.

People often turn to quick fixes to relieve their stress. These can produce a short, temporary relief but don't actually remove the cause of one's discomfort. Suppressants only increase one's stress level in the long run.

• Coffee and Cigarettes

The caffeine in coffee and the nicotine in cigarettes both stimulate the body's neuroendocrine system. This is also what

stress does. The result is increased blood pressure, pulse rate and anxiety. The initial pleasant stimulation experienced is achieved at the expense of using up the body's energy reserves.

• Alcohol, tranquillisers and sleeping pills

These have the opposite effects of coffee and cigarettes. They depress the body's neuroendocrine system. Initially they do relieve stress, but over a long period they will cause increased anxiety and depression. They also slow reaction time and impair co-ordination and judgement. Tolerance can develop to these drugs and they can become addictive. Also, their excessive use can cause diseases of the liver, nervous system and other body parts.

Coffee and alcohol in strict moderation will cause no harm, but keep away from cigarettes, tranquillisers and sleeping pills. If you are taking tranquillisers or sleeping pills, gradually reduce the dosage, with the co-operation of your doctor.

Note: Keep in mind that all the five drugs mentioned will reduce the quality of your sleep, so your body will be less able to cope with stress, thus defeating the very purpose of the drugs.

HIGHLIGHTS

- Stress release increases our vitality and health levels, making us look younger and feel better. It also makes us more productive, successful and have better relationships with other people.

- Stress is both physical and mental. Stress in one causes increased stress in the other which causes even more stress in the first one. The vicious cycle is set up.

- To become more stress-resistant, adopt a positive attitude to all situations and develop a healthy nervous system. A healthy nervous system is the result of good sleep, good nutrition, aerobic-type exercise and yoga or any other muscle relaxation.

- Stress suppressants have no lasting effect. In the long run, they damage your health.

- Try relaxation techniques.

CHAPTER 3

THE HABIT OF RESTFUL AWARENESS

Two monks came to a shallow river and were about to cross when they noticed a young woman. She explained to them that she was too scared to walk across the river. One of the monks said, "Don't worry, just jump on my back and I'll take you across."

After the monks had continued their journey for some time, the other monk said, " You shouldn't have taken that young lady on your back across the river. You know we are forbidden to associate with women."

The monk replied, "I left that woman behind at the river bank; you have not."

You understand stress and know various ways of releasing it. You look after your health. You relax. The easy feeling makes you feel good for a while, perhaps for a day or two, even a week. Then, as everyone says, life takes over. Again, you experience mood swings; once more, fear and anxiety take hold. You realise you haven't emptied your bag of regrets and grudges.

This is where the ultimate maintenance regimen for a productive but tranquil existence comes in.

You need to form the habit of restful awareness. This is done through meditation.

Meditate your way, not just out of chronic stress, but into a higher level of consciousness from where you can calmly and correctly assess the various aspects of your life. Only after you have reviewed and resolved inner conflicts brought on by excessive wishes, ego-tripping, long-standing grudges, low self-esteem and the desire to control other people's lives will your life become truly enjoyable.

The meditation habit results in a life of alert and joyful tranquillity.

SIMPLE & EFFORTLESS

Most of us have a vague idea what meditation is. Unfortunately, it has suffered an image problem in the past. People have associated it with eastern religions, severe concentration, psychic powers and even a withdrawal from the mainstream of life. Good-bye to fun, that sort of thing.

Here are the facts: Meditation has been a part of all religions, including Christianity, since religion began. It does not involve severe concentration. We do not meditate for the purpose of producing psychic powers. If they do occur, they are considered

merely a side effect. Withdrawing from the mainstream of life is just the opposite of what we are trying to achieve when we meditate. By bringing out our full potential, meditation allows us to enjoy life to the fullest. We do not have to retreat to caves for our sessions — the same results are reaped when we meditate in the comfort of our homes.

Anyone can meditate.   Meditation is a simple, natural and effortless technique for **quietening the mind**, making us experience an inner peace and leading us to connect with our True Self. The trouble is we have been conditioned to think that only complicated things yield beneficial effects. This is nonsense.

Meditation is simple because it works in harmony with your true nature or your higher consciousness. The mechanism for happiness is already there. All you have to do is use a technique to activate it. The meditation technique I recommend in Chapter 7 is a very powerful, time-efficient and safe way of doing this. It's a time honoured technique, having proven itself for thousands of years.

LIFE IS LIKE CARRYING TWO HEAVY SUITCASES

We are like a person who spends his whole life being **weighed down** by carrying two heavy suitcases. One is filled with thoughts of the **past** (regrets and guilt) and the other is filled with thoughts of the **future** (worries and expectations). A person who carries two heavy bags all day will be **tired** all day. We even carry these two suitcases to bed with us.

To have a rest from the burden of carrying these two suitcases **we need to put them down for a short while** to have a rest. Even just putting them down for ten or fifteen minutes makes us feel refreshed and stops our arms from aching.

When we **meditate** we put both suitcases down for a while and have a rest. **When we pick the suitcases up again,** they feel lighter, even though nothing has been taken out of them. They feel lighter because our minds have been rested. Similarly, **after meditation**, we feel refreshed, as though our burdens have been lifted, even though the "problems" have not been taken away.

After each meditation, the burden becomes lighter still and we become more energetic as the effects of meditation flow increasingly into our lives.

THE AUTHORITATIVE SOURCE OF MEDITATION

In around 500BC, the Indian Sage, Patanjali, wrote a treatise on life, which consisted of 196 brief statements, called *sutras*. In the masterpiece are profound metaphysical concepts condensed to their utmost limit. They describe the whole situation we call life, why we suffer and, more importantly, how to live from the blissful state of our Real Self. Indeed, this work pierces the very veil of reality.

Patanjali was not the originator of the content of this treatise, but in it he sums up the total knowledge of the sages and yogis. I do not recommend that you try to read it. It doesn't make for light reading, since it was written for yogis who were already well advanced. They just needed a **summary** of the nature of life, and how to attain cosmic consciousness.

Patanjali explains that it's **thought waves** which prevent us from living from our true nature or Real Self. **We identify with our thought waves** and we live from this False Self, which we refer to as the **ego.** When the mind is still, the Real Self, which is our Higher Consciousness, can shine through. This is a gradual process which takes place over many years.

I will now give a few selected **sutras** from Patanjali's work, to illustrate how, with brilliant economy and intellect, he explains the yogis' view on life and how to achieve the blissful state of enlightenment.

Sutra 2: "Yoga is the inhibition of the modifications of the mind."

Modifications refer to the different types of thought waves.

Sutra 3: "Then the Seer is established in his own essential nature."

When there are no thought waves, the Seer has attained Self realisation and is now living from his Real Self.

Sutra 4: "In other states there is assimilation (of the Seer) with the modifications (of the mind)."

When you are not living from your true nature, you identify yourself with whatever your thoughts are. Since thoughts are largely due to historic conditioning from your particular past circumstances, they are not the real you.

Sutra 54: "The lack of awareness of Reality, the sense of egoism, attractions and repulsions towards objects and the strong desire for life, are the great afflictions or causes of all miseries in life."

When we live from the level of our ego and we all do to a greater or lesser extent, we lack awareness of our Real Self, and this produces attachment to things in life, resulting in unhappiness.

The **last sutra** states that the final stage of meditation produces enlightenment and this occurs when we are living from our Real nature which is pure consciousness.

It should be noted that Patanjali, as with other Seers, does not recommend that we try to suppress our thoughts. Trying to still the mind forcibly does not work. All the Seers agree that there are only two ways to reduce thought waves. One is to observe your thoughts passively by detaching yourself from them. The other is meditation.

WHY MEDITATE?

Scientists like to define meditation as a state of restful alertness. The mind is relaxed, yet still alert. It is often called the meditative state of consciousness, because it is different from our normal waking and sleeping consciousness. We are calm and energetic at the same time.

Many among us are like a person lost in a jungle. He can't see the way out of the jungle because he sees only the trees around him. These trees are his problems. They surround and tend to overwhelm him. If he should climb a big tree and gets above the line of the other trees, he would see where he is and the way out. Meditation is like climbing this tall tree. We rise above all the little problems and our mind becomes clearer, enabling us to work our way out of our predicament. Meditation allows us to see the big picture.

Since the mind is the source of unhappiness and happiness, stress and calm, sickness and well-being, failure and success, it is logical that we should direct our attention to the mind. Even doctors admit that at least 70% of physical diseases are psychosomatic, that is, they originate in the mind. So for every 10 people who declare themselves sick, seven suffer from illnesses which originate in the mind, whether spurred by fear, worry, anger, jealousy or some other negative emotion.

The feeling of peace, of being more centred and in tune with nature cannot really be ascribed or understood by the logical mind. We will discuss this in Chapter 5, The Ego & The Chattering Mind.

WON'T THE CALMNESS MAKE US LETHARGIC?

Definitely not. In fact, the opposite will happen. Becoming calmer will energise you at the same time.

Times of anxiety and panic waste energy. Tense muscles, overactive nerves and a mind in overdrive dent our energy reserves.

But calmness and vitality are complementary. People who are "hyper" may seem energetic but they are actually fuelled by nervous energy. They end up irritable and mentally exhausted.

You will feel the beneficial effects of meditation even after your first session. The effects are subtle and cumulative so every month you will find yourself a little less stressed and a little happier.

AREN'T WE ESCAPING FROM REALITY?

If reality is worry, anxiety, regrets and guilt feelings, then, yes, meditation is an escape from this type of 'reality'. We have become so accustomed to these negative states of mind we assume they make up the real world.

But there really is a better way of living. This 'other reality' emerges when our higher consciousness is allowed to shine through.

This higher consciousness works in harmony with nature. Therefore, the increased mind power it unfolds cannot be used to harm others.

MEDITATION EXPANDS YOUR CONSCIOUSNESS

When thought is reduced by meditation, the higher consciousness is given a chance to infuse into your mind.

The higher consciousness is a very real thing. We experience glimpses of it at various stages of our lives — moments of utter peacefulness, feelings of bliss. This is the higher consciousness expressing itself. Because our minds live on the thinking level, these moments are rare, if they ever happen at all.

Intuition is the intelligence of your higher consciousness and is far more accurate than normal thought. Some of you may be wondering: *But we need to think to perform our daily tasks!* You think wrong. When the phone rings, you don't tell yourself: *I will now pick up the receiver.* You do it automatically. Your innate intelligence responds to the ringing of the telephone.

In fact, when your mind is crowded with thoughts, the functioning of your innate intelligence is impeded. That's when you rush towards the phone when it is the doorbell ringing.

CAN WE REMAIN MATERIALISTIC?

Of course, you can go on liking possessions. But your attitude towards them will be marked by a healthy detachment: they serve you, you don't serve them. You can go on wishing to have this or that, to go here and there, but your desires will be tempered with reason. A more serene outlook makes you less disposed to buying things you can ill-afford. It stops you keeping up with your greedy neighbour.

When you become less stressed and you are living more from your higher consciousness, you enjoy everything more — including material things. If you don't feel good inside, how can you enjoy things outside?

The whole basis of meditation is to make you enjoy life more. To do this, we have to tap our physical, mental and spiritual potential.

The beauty of meditation is that it makes you happy inside, so you are happy anyway, irrespective of whether you are materialistic or not. Your happiness is not dependent on external factors. So you get not only happiness, but freedom also.

Happiness comes from within and unless we give attention to what's inside us, we will remain stressed and unhappy. This is regardless of our economic situation. If we are wealthy, we enjoy our riches more. If we aren't wealthy, we will enjoy an increased creativity and productivity. This should help improve our financial situation.

WHAT CHANGES SHOULD WE EXPECT?

Obviously, we change for the better.

Some people worry because they fear change and want to remain "themselves". The important point to realise is that the changes brought about by meditation are natural and subtle. We start living more from our full potential gradually. This full potential is our Natural or Real Self.

Scientists claim we are living from approximately 5% of our full potential. How can this be the real you — 95% of you is untapped! We are living from about 5% of our intelligence potential, 5% of our vitality potential and 5% of our happiness potential. We only know this part of us and totally identify with this measly 5% and think: *This is me.*

WHAT HAPPENS TO OUR LIFESTYLE?

Because meditation causes you to connect with your Real Self or Natural Self, you will, gradually, feel an increasing desire to live more in harmony with nature. You will tend to gravitate towards a simpler lifestyle.

You will desire more natural things such as nourishing food, fresh air and exercise. If you smoke or drink alcohol excessively, your taste for these vices will diminish. You will stop overeating.

Meditation causes your innate intelligence or what the yogis call the life force to manifest itself more strongly. This results in an urge to live more in accordance with nature's laws.

Since your mind is less cluttered with unnecessary thoughts, you get more focused and your goals are clarified.

Our relationships with other people also improve. We cease

to worry about other people hurting us. In any case, we will tend to attract people who can only make us happier.

WHEN THE REAL SELF REPLACES THE EGO

When our mind calms down and our higher consciousness starts expressing itself, we tend to become less subjective and more objective. Our small ego self becomes a Larger Self.

This has been recorded by several poets, among them William Wordsworth and Alfred Lord Tennyson. Tennyson practised a form of mantra meditation where he used to repeat his own name. This produced for him a feeling of ecstasy in which he saw "unity in all things." In one account, he wrote: *The individual itself seemed to resolve and fade away into boundless being, and this not a confused state, but the clearest of the clearest, utterly beyond words, where death an almost laughable impossibility, the loss of personality (if so it were) seeming no extinction, but the only true life.*

What Tennyson "saw" was exactly what other meditation masters have reported when in a state of higher consciousness. For a brief moment, the "normal personality" is replaced by a feeling of oneness with all things. You don't feel any loss of yourself, indeed, this feels like the Real Self.

The ultimate goal of meditation is to live continuously in this blissful state. Of course, this is a long, long way down the track. For now, let us be content with being less stressed.

HOW TO STOP WORRYING RIGHT NOW

It will take a few meditation sessions to release your deep-seated chronic stress and produce a worry-free mind. Until this occurs I thought it would be useful to give you two valuable techniques which will break the worry habit right now.

Firstly, when you start to think of the future and are on the brink of anxiety, just say to yourself, "**we'll see**". Two small words, yet they can prevent a lot of worry. You do not know what is going to happen tomorrow or further down the track so why worry about what might or might not happen. We worry because it is a **habit** and the best way to **break the habit** is to replace any worry thought with the positive expression "we'll see".

I'll explain why this technique works so well. The vast majority of our worries never eventuate and that is a fact. Even though they are a figment of our imagination, they cause a lot of distress and can bring on health problems and premature ageing. Since, in general, worries do not eventuate, it is pointless to worry. By saying "we'll see", every time you think of some possible future event, the mind will eventually give up worrying since it has learned not to project itself into the future.

The other way this technique works is based on the fact that **whatever we think about we tend to attract.** In other words, if we fear, we will tend to attract that fear. This is especially so, if we keep worrying about the same thing. This principle feeds on repetition. But by replacing a worry with "we'll see", we are no longer giving power to that worry; nor are we enticing that worry to happen.

Another good expression to use to replace worry is "**forget results**". If you are in business and worrying about how business will go this week, replace that worry with the thought, "forget results". You see, the cause of success is one of application. If you are working on a project and worry about results, you are not applying to it the hundred per cent concentration the project deserves. The worrying makes you omit things and make mistakes. Concentrate on what you are doing. If you do the right things, that is, the cause is taken care of, **results will take care of themselves.** This expression gives us great relief, since we can now put all our attention on the causes of success and stop wasting time on worrying.

HIGHLIGHTS

- Meditation is a **natural, simple, effortless** technique for **quietening the mind** and **connecting with our True Self.** It results in **inner peace, happiness** and living increasingly from our **full potential.**

- Since the **mind** is the root cause of stress, failure and unhappiness as well as calmness, success and happiness, it's logical we should direct our attention to the mind. Meditation has a more **powerful beneficial effect** on the mind than any other known activity.

- Meditation is so **simple** that anyone can do it. It's also very **natural** — it requires no drugs or equipment and costs nothing.

- Meditation is **different from relaxation techniques** since it produces a deeper level of relaxation and **unfolds** our **Higher Consciousness.**

- You will feel the beneficial effects even **after your first meditation** and since the effects are **cumulative**, you will experience increasing benefits as time goes by.

- Meditation causes you to **enjoy everything more, including material things**, but your happiness no longer depends on these things any more, since you are **happier inside** anyway.

CHAPTER 4

MEDITATE REJUVENATE

Health is not valued until sickness comes.

Thomas Fuller

Meditation is the best time investment you can make. If you believe that health is wealth, then the two fifteen-minute periods a day you set aside for your sessions will make you a rich person.

Many studies have shown that meditation significantly improves our health level. The stress release and the deep rest produced when we meditate activate the body's own healing forces.

All healing comes from within. Drugs merely suppress the symptoms and often do nothing to remove the cause of the problem. In fact, there are cases when drugs produce side effects, thereby aggravating the situation.

There are, of course, instances when medication is needed. People suffering from diabetes, heart or respiratory diseases, kidney or liver problems , need conventional medical supervision. Certain tumours are better surgically removed. When this happens, a positive attitude towards the prescribed treatment is advised.

Meditation is an excellent complement to conventional medicine or surgery. Patients who meditate don't malinger; they heal themselves faster.

People think they are healthy because they are not sick. Wellness is more than just not having a cold or the 'flu. It has more to do with energy levels, vitality and the enthusiasm for life.

WHEN SLEEP DOES NOT PROVIDE SUFFICIENT REST

Theoretically, we should wake up every morning feeling fresh and alive and ready to tackle whatever the day has in store for us. But as we all too well know, this is not always the case. The problem is we don't always sleep deeply enough or for long

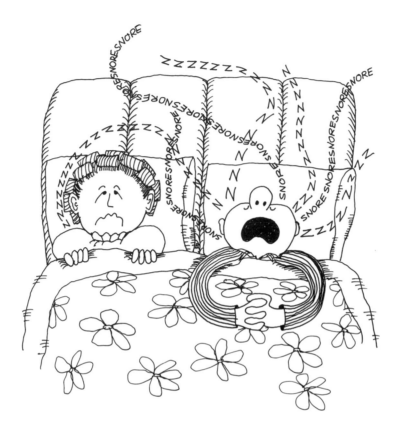

enough. Physical discomfort, mental worries or just not feeling relaxed, can prevent a good night's sleep.

This is where meditation comes to the rescue. By giving our nervous system an **additional** period of deep rest twice a day, we compensate for a bad night's sleep, so we still feel good and have a productive day.

Studies show that during both sleep and meditation, our metabolic rate slows down. The metabolic rate refers to how quickly the body uses oxygen to "burn up" the nutrients from foods to produce energy. A low metabolic rate indicates the body is not using up much oxygen and is in a more restful state. In other words, the metabolic rate is a good indicator on how rested the body is.

The remarkable thing is that meditation produces a lower metabolic rate than sleep. During sleep, it takes four or five hours to produce an 8% drop in metabolic rate, while during a thirty minute meditation, we achieve a drop of between **10% and 20%**. This means **meditation produces a much deeper state of rest than sleep and in a much shorter time**. In addition, alpha waves are produced by the brain in meditation, also signifying a deep state of rest. Alpha waves do not usually occur during sleep.

This does not mean you don't need sleep. You do, for sleep has many other functions besides producing rest and is essential for our well-being.

When the nervous system is rested by meditation, our brain works at peak efficiency. This means we display more **intelligence**, more **creativity** and more **feelings**. This is especially significant, since **happiness** and **success** depend to a large extent on these three factors.

Deep rest also makes us feel good since it relaxes the nervous system and allows it to be **recharged with energy**. The world all of a sudden feels Okay. The problem we thought we could not solve no longer appears monstrous. We feel good and that is far more important. We see the **"Big Picture"** and are not weighed down by temporary problems. The day goes smoothly and nothing seems to ruffle us. This is because stress has been released from the nervous system and a stress-free nervous system can handle the ups and downs of life.

HOW MEDITATION PRODUCES DEEP REST

The deep rest produced by meditation is due mainly to the **reduction in thought** when we meditate. Thoughts actually produce waves which are registered in the brain as **electrical activity**. If our thoughts are excessive and in most of us they are, then this electrical activity becomes excessive and is a **disturbance** to the brain. We feel this as unpleasantness in the mind. We call this unpleasant feeling, stress.

Meditation greatly reduces the amount of electrical activity in the brain. The brain becomes calm and we feel this in the mind as a pleasant peacefulness.

In other words, the brain is given a rest which allows it to recuperate and rejuvenate.

PROOF THAT MEDITATION RELEASES STRESS

Electrical activity of the brain can be measured by an electroencephalogram. Wires are connected from this instrument to the scalp and forehead.

In a study done by Dr A Kasamatsu and Dr T Hirai of the University of Tokyo, it was found that when Zen monks meditated, they produced a predominance of alpha waves. In addition, the alpha waves increased in amplitude and regularity during meditation. This same effect was found by researchers in India when they did studies on Yogis during meditation.

This predominance of alpha waves is associated with a state of deep relaxation and a feeling of well-being. It verifies that meditation is extremely effective in releasing stress.

DEEP REST PRODUCES REJUVENATION

Deep rest activates the body's own healing forces allowing rejuvenation of the body to occur. Once the metabolic rate slows down, the body can now direct some of its energy for healing and rejuvenation. Previously, all its energy was required for bodily functions.

We become **healthier**. Minor and sometimes major health disorders disappear and we start to **look and feel younger**. **Disease** is actually a very apt word. It implies that not being at ease, **dis. . .ease**, is stressful and is a major factor in illnesses.

Not only the body, but the mind also rejuvenates. For probably the first time in your life, your mind, through meditation, is getting a rest during the day. Body and mind have in-built abilities to rejuvenate — they just need the right conditions. Meditation provides you the key.

The stress release achieved through meditation brings about some very important health benefits:

Improved Sleep

We fall asleep quicker and our sleep is deeper. This means we get more and better quality sleep. As a result, we wake up feeling fresher and more alive.

Reduced Blood Pressure

The release of stress causes our muscles to relax, including the muscular walls of our blood vessels. This means more blood can pump through the vessels and there is less resistance to the

PRODUCES DEEPER REST THAN SLEEP

REACTIVATES THE BODY'S OWN HEALING FORCES

RAISES OUR VITALITY LEVELS

HELPS ASTHMA PATIENTS

overall flow . This of course means less blood pressure. High blood pressure, of course, is well recognised as a major factor in producing heart diseases and heart attacks.

In an American study on stress management, 35 people with an average systolic blood pressure of 146 were placed under observation. After just a few weeks of meditation, their blood pressure had dropped to 137. A drop of almost 10 points is very significant, lowering the blood pressure from the borderline high range to the normal range. This is far better than taking drugs which have side effects and do nothing to address the cause of the problem.

It's my opinion that if you combine meditation with a good diet — especially a low fat, low salt diet, take garlic tablets and do some aerobic-type exercise such as brisk walking — you can stop taking blood pressure drugs. The exceptions, obviously, are the chronically ill. At any rate, all such activity, if you are taking prescribed drugs, should be conducted in consultation with your doctor.

EFFECT OF STRESS

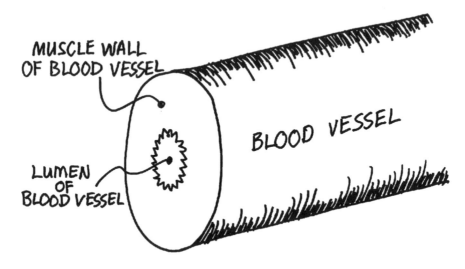

MUSCLE WALL
OF BLOOD VESSEL

BLOOD VESSEL

LUMEN
OF
BLOOD VESSEL

STRESS CAUSES CONTRACTION OF MUSCULAR WALL OF BLOOD VESSEL RESULTING IN NARROWING OF BLOOD VESSEL. THIS CAUSES HIGH BLOOD PRESSURE.

EFFECT OF MEDITATION

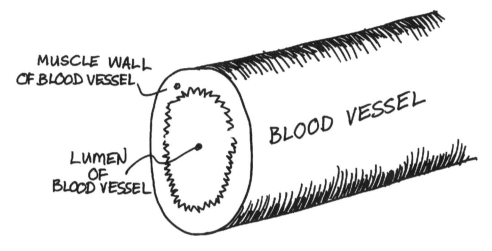

MUSCLE WALL OF BLOOD VESSEL

BLOOD VESSEL

LUMEN OF BLOOD VESSEL

MEDITATION CAUSES RELAXATION OF MUSCULAR WALL OF BLOOD VESSEL RESULTING IN REDUCED NARROWING OF BLOOD VESSEL.

Increased Circulation to All Organs and Glands

Relaxed blood vessels allow increased blood flow to all our body parts. Increased blood flow to the brain means we feel fresher and can think more clearly. It also helps to prevent strokes. Increased blood flow to the digestive system means it will function better and we will digest and assimilate food better.

Balances The Two Hemispheres of The Brain

Studies show meditation has a balancing effect on the right and left hemispheres of the brain. Our left hemisphere is responsible for thinking. It is the logical analytical side of the brain, The right side is responsible for feelings. Due to the nature of modern life, many of us tend to be left hemisphere people. That is, we think too much and analyse too much, at the expense of our feelings.

Meditation will allow us to have the right balance of logical analytical thought and feelings.

Stimulates Hormonal Activity

Meditation stimulates our glands to produce more hormones. In fact, studies show that hormone levels in meditators are similar to those in people up to ten years younger. This is one of the reasons why meditators look and feel younger. At the same time, meditation causes a reduction in the production of our stress hormones — adrenaline and noradrenaline.

Assists Health Problems

Up to 70% of health problems are psychosomatic, that is, they have a mental origin, so it is not difficult to imagine how reduced stress from meditation can help many of these disorders.

Helps Asthma

A clinical research conducted by Ron Honsberger and Archie F. Wilson in the USA reported that asthmatic patients showed improvement in their asthma after starting meditation. Ninety four percent of the group showed less airways resistance measurements, 55% showed improvement as reported by their personal physicians and 74% stated they themselves felt an improvement.

Meditation Protects Your Teeth

In an American study, a group of people were subjected to stress, which resulted in their saliva containing proteins involved in the formation of plaque. Plaque is a bacterial coating which causes cavities in the teeth.

The same people did twenty minutes meditation and it was found they had lower levels of plaque-forming bacteria in their mouths. Even more surprising, their saliva had high levels of calcium, phosphorous and fluoride — all of which protect enamel.

REVERSAL OF THE AGEING PROCESS

Biomechanical age measures how old a person is physiologically. As a group, long-term meditators who had been practising meditation for more than five years were physiologically 12 years younger than their chronological age, as measured by reduction of blood pressure, and better near-point vision and auditory discrimination. Short-term meditators were physiologically five years younger than their chronological age. The study, conducted in the United States, took into consideration the effects of diet and exercise.

RESTFUL ALERTNESS

In their electroencephalographic studies, the French team of Jean-Paul Banquet and Maurice Sailhan reported that, during meditation, a greater proportion of alpha waves were produced compared to delta waves. This indicates a heightened level of wakefulness. In addition, the ratio of beta waves to alpha waves was reduced, indicating a more relaxed state.

It's this unique combination of deep relaxation and yet increased alertness that differentiates meditation from other relaxation techniques and sleep. It is referred to as the meditative state of consciousness or the super-conscious state. It indicates the emergence of the higher consciousness.

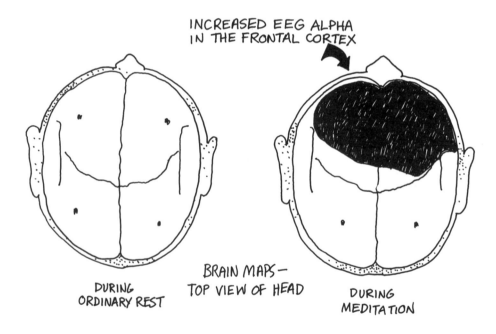

INCREASED EEG ALPHA
IN THE FRONTAL CORTEX

DURING
ORDINARY REST

BRAIN MAPS —
TOP VIEW OF HEAD

DURING
MEDITATION

The electroencephalograph (EEG) brain maps above illustrate the findings of several studies published in various science journals showing that meditation increases the EEG index of restful alertness — increased slow alpha frequency power in the frontal cortex. This change in the EEG indicates a relaxed state of wakefulness during meditation, an ordered state of brain functioning that is ideal preparation for dynamic activity.

OPTIMISING OF BRAIN FUNCTIONING

Reports published in the International Journal of Neuroscience claim that higher levels of EEG coherence measured during the practice of meditation are significantly correlated with increased fluency of verbal creativity, increased efficiency in learning new concepts, more principled moral reasoning, higher verbal IQ, decreased neuroticism, clearer experiences of transcendental consciousness and increased neurological efficiency.

MEDITATION REDUCES DRUG ADDICTION

A study on the effects of meditation on drug use was undertaken in the United States by Dr R K Wallace, Dr H Benson and Associates. Two questionnaires were sent to almost 2000 people who were experienced meditators. About 1800 people responded. The subjects were asked to record their drug-use habits before starting meditation and after.

In the six-month period prior to starting meditation, 78% had used marijuana and hashish or both and 28% of this group were heavy users (once a day or more). After six months meditation, only 37% continued to use marijuana — that's a 40% drop. After 21 months of meditation, only 12% continued to use marijuana — a 66% drop. Of those who still took drugs only one was a heavy user.

Meditation was even more successful with LSD users. After 22 months of meditation, 97% of LSD users had given it up.

There was also a high rate of success with heavy narcotics, including heroin, opium, morphine and cocaine. Before meditation, 17% used these drugs and after a 22 to 23 month period of meditation, only 1% continued to use them.

When questioned why the meditators gave up drugs the general response was they interfered with the profound feelings from meditation, which they enjoyed more.

HIGHLIGHTS

- Meditation produces a rest deeper than sleep and in a much shorter time. This causes our brain to work at peak efficiency so we display more intelligence, creativity and feelings. It also makes us feel good since deep rest relaxes the nervous system and recharges it with energy.

- Deep rest reactivates the body's own healing forces, allowing rejuvenation of the body and mind to occur.

- Meditation raises our vitality levels; it makes us healthier.

CHAPTER 5

THE EGO & THE CHATTERING MIND

A young man entered a very strict monastery. He was told of the rules. One of them was that he would be allowed one sentence every seven years and he was to speak only to the abbot. On the appointed day, his progress would be assessed.

After seven years, the monk thought of something profound to tell the abbot, but, when he entered the room, he blurted out the first thing on his mind. He said, "The food here is terrible."

Another seven years went by. On his second visit, he was determined to say something philosophical and brilliant, but, once more, he let out what was on his mind. He said, "The beds are very hard."

Still another seven years passed. After twenty one years, the student felt confident that he had progressed enough to impress the abbot. He practised his enlightened statement a day before their meeting. He rehearsed the whole day. But, once in the presence of his superior, his mind seized him and he yelled, "I've had enough of this place. I'm getting out."

The abbot nodded. "Good decision," the old man said. "You've done nothing but complain the whole time you've been here."

A re you ready for meditation?

Although everybody can meditate, there are people who are more prepared for it than others. I am not talking here about organising rooms and meditation cushions — these are small details that take a few minutes to settle.

I'm talking about preparing *yourself*. This is more important than the location of your meditation sessions or whether you'll sit in a chair or on a cushion on the floor.

Pre-disposing yourself to meditation maximises its beneficial effects.

You may be impatient to begin, but impatience will only delay the benefits each session ought to bring.

THE MAIN OBSTACLES TO MEDITATION

Two obstacles should be addressed in your preparations. Plainly defined, these are the ego and the chattering mind.

There are other obstacles, like being unable to organise time or having an aversion to anything that requires a little discipline. These hurdles have their roots in the ego problem.

THE EGO

Meditation replaces the ego gradually with the higher consciousness. Its eventual extinction worries the ego and it will therefore tend to resist change. You'll find yourself making all sorts of excuses why you cannot meditate — a demanding career, a problematic family life, a sick relative, a toothache, anything. Or you simply declare that you don't need to meditate at all.

BEGINNINGS OF THE EGO

The ego originates from infancy. Once the umbilical cord is cut, we start our quest for identity. As babies we get identified with our earliest possessions — *his* bottle, *her* diapers, *his* pram, *her* crib. Then we learn to claim ownership — *my* toys, *my* dog, *my* blanket, *my* room. The ego begins with this concept of territory and possession. We will cling to *our* toys; we will protect *our* dog; we will get annoyed if somebody uses *our* blanket and we will get very, very upset if somebody is made to share *our* room.

Already we see some characteristics of the early ego — possessiveness, jealousy, competitiveness and aggression. From childhood, life becomes one of possessiveness, competition, rivalry, struggle, conflict and aggression.

The whole problem of the ego originates from when we consider ourselves separate from everyone else — *These are my toys*, etc. This goes against the whole concept of the universe which is *unity*, where everything is interconnected. Plants give off oxygen which we breathe in and they take in the carbon dioxide which we breathe out. When we identify ourselves as being separate, we produce conflict not only with each other, but also with the reality of the universe.

Remember the ego's definitions — it is the self in contrast with another person; the consciousness of the self and its development; the part of the mind concerned with the perception of external reality and with adjusting responses to it.

EXERCISES TO SOLVE THE EGO PROBLEM

Do you usually complete sentences for other people?

Do you half- listen to somebody's story and in the middle of it tell yourself, what a silly thing to share?

Do you find yourself building your argument silently while the other person is explaining his/her side?

We think we listen, but do we? Half the time we are preparing to say the next thing. Worse, sometimes we keep on talking and don't notice that somebody else wants to have a word.

Egoists don't really listen. Egoists are judgemental.

Exercise 1

Set aside times for quiet, wholehearted listening. You could be talking to anybody — a colleague, your spouse, your child, your mother-in-law, a friend.

Let the person talk and finish what he/she has to say. Do not interrupt; don't make comments.

Follow the rhythm of the speech; follow the inflections.

You'll find it difficult at first, but persevere. When you are tempted to interrupt somebody in mid-sentence, it's the ego at work. Silence it.

Give it five minutes, ten minutes at a time. Little by little you will realise the pleasantness of quiet listening. You'll be convinced that the exercise should extend in all your conversations.

This exercise will curb your impatience and will help a lot when you start meditating. You will be fidgeting less. You will feel easy about the duration of your session; you will not be sitting there with your mind's eye on the clock.

Exercise 2

There are many instances when you find yourself in the company of people who may not be "on the same wave length". Again it is the ego asserting itself, telling you that you're smarter, wittier, better-dressed, more knowledgeable.

These are the times when you make silent, sweeping judgements.

Take a situation when somebody is saying something that

strikes you as ridiculous. Your usual "smart" response is to sit there with a mental half-smirk.

Over the voices, the mind's commentary runs: How awful, it says, how pathetic!

On these occasions, when you're feeling mightily superior to those around you, tell yourself, **Drop the ego.**

Every time you think you are tempted to look down on present company, remind yourself, **Drop the ego.**

This is a good exercise for those who are wondering why people appear hesitant in their presence. Mental half-smirks give off signals. We call them vibes. Vibes are real. If your vibes are negative or hostile, of course, people feel uneasy in your company.

So, tell yourself, **drop the ego.**

This exercise is another good preparation for meditation. You will not feel awkward about having to sit still for a quarter of an hour. You will not be asking, whatever for? You will not feel embarrassed about wanting to release stress. You will not conceal your need to be tranquil.

Exercise 3

The layer of chronic stress that leaves us feeling constantly dissatisfied and unhappy is actually a build-up of unresolved emotions.

The ego can be very arrogant. It refuses to own up to feelings, particularly if they aren't flattering ones. You have heard people say they never bear grudges and in the same breath recall for your benefit hurts of two decades ago.

Memories of early deprivation, animosities spurred by sibling rivalries, deep-seated resentments against parents and spouses, residual anger left by conflicts with others, the unresolved acrimony of bad relationships — they sit in the subconscious from where they occasionally spit out venom.

But we are proud egoists and say, "I'm happy as I am."

We can spend a whole lifetime going around in circles, recreating situations, duplicating antagonisms and repeating emotionally damaging mistakes without ever really taking time to consider what we've been about.

Take stock. Sit down for a few minutes, breathing deeply. Concentrate. In this quiet, talk to yourself, ask questions. Let the images surface, let the subconscious spill its awful contents.

Own up to feelings you have long denied. It's not flattering to see you're a nag or you're jealous or you're spiteful. But continued denial only increases the depth of your chronic stress.

Tell yourself, I want to stop being a nag. Or, I want to be rid of these grudges. Or, I want to forgive him (or her) for all that. Or, I want to forgive myself for such and such.

Purging your system of long-standing hurts and displeasures — the process is called *catharsis* — prepares you for the full benefits of meditation. Catharsis opens up the valves of your being into which the radiance of the higher consciousness can filter during your sittings.

Chronic stress is like plaque in the nervous system. Meditation does a flossing job that steadily gets rid of the accumulated dirt. But the flossing can be done most effectively only after we've acknowledged the presence of plaque.

THE CHATTERING MIND

Sit down quietly. Close your eyes. Just for a few minutes, try *not* to think. Impossible!

This illustrates how little control we have over our minds. The thoughts arise without our consent and without any selection.

The overwhelming thing you'll notice when you start meditating is the constant chattering of the mind. Indeed, large numbers of people lose heart and stop meditating because they get defeated by their overly active minds.

We love to verbalise things. We see a rose and, immediately, the mind runs a commentary on it — "What a beautiful flower. What a fragrant rose." In thinking these thoughts, we are actually missing the real experience of a beautiful and fragrant flower.

When we are told to relax and find time to smell the roses, we are being urged to experience the roses, not to comment on them. There is a big difference.

Thoughts are not the object we are looking at; thoughts are second-hand, old, a result of past conditioning. We look at a rose and our verbalising becomes part of our memory so the next time we see another one, the same responses are evoked. Our commentary on a particular rose draws from a bank of linguistic memories of other roses we have commented on in the past. How do we react? What do we say when we look at a rose? We exclaim: How pretty, how sweet!

Our lives are piles of old, mechanical responses to the things around us. No wonder we complain of being bored! But we cannot seem to stop the mind from constantly making the same tired comments.

The Experience Vs The Commentary

Our minds tend to spend too much time thinking of an event rather than experiencing it. We have opinions and judgements. Think of the times when you watch a game on TV. There is the direct experience of the game and there is the running commentary by some expert. What usually happens?

You begin "arguing" with the commentator! Now, he is giving you his opinions. Whether he is right or wrong is irrelevant, but you have been sidetracked — your direct experience of watching the match is tarnished.

Of course, it is natural to have comments after the experience but the problem is, with most of us, the commentary takes up more space in the mind than the experience itself. We therefore take the commentary to be the reality and we miss the experience.

Meditation will show us the difference between the reality and the interpretation. It stills the mind, allowing us to experience the reality of a situation. Thinking is the interpretation. It is, if you like, our bias.

How we experience life is our reality. The more stressed we are, the more clouded that reality is. When the inner commentaries cease, we experience life with our intuition and feelings — this makes our days more pleasurable.

Silencing the Chattering Mind

Become aware of your constant verbalising and train yourself slowly to see other people and things without commenting or judging. It will be a rewarding experience because for probably the first time you'll see things from a new and fresh perspective.

Exercise 1

Next time you find yourself looking at a seascape (or anything beautiful), just look at it. Stand there and feel the sun or the wind on your face. If waves are lapping on the shore, just listen.

You will come away refreshed and relaxed because you will have truly experienced the magnificence of it. A gushing commentary will only create a barrier between the seascape and your appreciation.

Exercise 2

Listen to your favourite music, but listen. Don't make it serve as backdrop to your eating or your reading. Make it the event. Again, no exclamation points. Just your 100% attention.

Exercise 3

This exercise is excellent for those who say they cannot keep their minds still.

Sit down and decide to grant yourself a few minutes of silence.

The first thing you should realise is that you shouldn't even try to keep your mind still. It is a trying, futile exercise.

Don't try to stop thoughts since the struggle will only result in a ridiculous situation where the mind is fighting itself. This not only achieves nothing, but also creates added tension.

Just sit there and watch the mind. Let the thoughts come and go. It's like walking into a dark room. You don't fight the darkness; you turn the light on or light a torch and the darkness goes away. Similarly, when you don't fight but just become aware of the mind, the thoughts start fading and the chattering is lessened.

MOMENTS OF NO-MIND

Awareness does not mean judging, criticising or trying to control the mind. When you do this, you become involved with its restlessness and are no longer a detached observer. Give the mind total freedom. The awareness gradually produces a detachment from your thoughts. By not identifying with them, you are no longer empowering them to clutter your mind.

This exercise is essential to the preparation for meditation. When you meditate, your detachment gets strengthened and your awareness will become deeper and deeper. You will notice gaps between your thoughts. With these gaps, you will enjoy occasional glimpses of "no-mind", transitory peaks when you feel totally relaxed and released from all cares. These brief moments will give you a taste of bliss. They are brief and may be very rare but when they happen, you know you're on the right track. As you meditate more, you become more adept at watching the mind and the gaps become bigger and more frequent. The higher consciousness is now getting through.

Such peak moments are precious but let us not allow the ego to make much of them. Don't boast about them or start initiating enlightenment games. Don't talk enlightened; be it.

What is more important is the permanent tranquil plateau that sharpened perceptions and creative intelligence create through meditation. It's not the Mothers' Days or the Fathers' Days or the happy anniversaries that really matter. If your daily life is calm and joyful, you have a daily reason to celebrate.

As you progress, this awareness will gradually develop quite naturally. When the mind is clear, a deep awareness of things begins to emerge.

Modern physics and meditation are starting to converge. What the ancient meditation masters stated about the universe thousands of years ago — such as the fundamental basis of solid matter is energy and that pure consciousness is the underlying reality of the universe — is now being confirmed by Quantum physics. What was discovered about reality by meditation masters in the silence of their inner temples is now being confirmed by scientists in their laboratories. This has resulted in many scientists taking a spiritual view of the universe.

HIGHLIGHTS

- The ego and the chattering mind are the two main hindrances to meditation.

- Exercises to solve the ego problem.

- The difference between the direct experience and our commentary.

- Exercises to silence the chattering mind.

- Moments of no-mind — The more we meditate, the more drastically reduced our thoughts will be and our vision will be sharpened. We will experience moments of utter bliss.

CHAPTER 6

THE 2 MOST EFFECTIVE
MEDITATION TECHNIQUES

**The only true development is the
development of the Self.**

There are many different meditation techniques but the two I'm presenting in this book are the most effective for stress release. They are also very simple.

The technique I recommend is a combination of the two and is discussed in detail in the next chapter, Your Meditation Session.

1. THE TRANQUIL BREATHING MEDITATION

Observing the breath is an ancient technique with a very distinguished origin. It was started by the Buddha and was, in fact, his favourite meditation. It is still the main Buddhist meditation technique and has been adopted by many meditation schools since. This method has not been improved upon since it was originated.

It is also the most effective procedure to quieten the mind.

Lightly focus on your breathing at the tip of your nostrils. Observe the flow of the breath. . . in. . . and. . . out. . . at the entrance of the nostrils. Be aware of the breath the whole time it is going in and the whole time it is going out. When you pause between breaths, keep your attention at the nostrils. This helps to distract the mind from thinking. Put down the two suitcases of the past and the future for a few minutes. Put all your attention on the present, on the breath.

Here we are using the flow of the breath as an object to focus our attention on and therefore reduce thoughts and calm the mind. The breath is ideal for this purpose because it is natural and is intimately connected to our higher consciousness.

As you sustain your breath, the breath becomes more and more subtle. The body begins to feel lighter.

You emerge feeling refreshed.

Every session benefits you and the longer you meditate, the better you will feel. As the layers of acute and chronic stress dissolve, the higher consciousness begins manifesting itself. There will be times when the mind will actually be bright and joyful and the body will experience fleeting rapture. Gaps between thoughts may be filled with radiance. These are the rewards of meditation.

2. MANTRA MEDITATION

All you do is silently repeat a **meaningless word** to yourself. We choose a 'meaningless' word because it will not conjure up other ideas and start the thinking process.

We choose a mantra for its sound effect on the body. Sound is a vibration and if the correct vibration is chosen, it can have a very beneficial effect on the body. Take the example of music. The right music inspires finer feelings and lifts your spirits. There is also the effect of ultra-sound. The vibrating effects of a particular frequency has a healing effect on human tissues, reducing inflammation.

The Origin of Mantras

Mantras have their origin in the Sanskrit language of ancient India. The actual articulation was specially developed by the ancient seers, so that each sound of the alphabet would have a beneficial effect on the spiritual evolution of people.

According to occultists of all ages and cultures, there exists in the spinal column area a series of energy centres which are called *chakras*. Chakra is an old Sanskrit word that means *wheel*. It describes a circular spiralling field of energy. The yogis confirm the existence of these centres. These are the spiritual or evolutionary centres of the body, the site of our higher consciousness. These are non-physical and therefore cannot be detected by our physical senses.

Increased brain
alpha waves
(relaxation waves)

Reduced metabolic rate
(indicates deep rest)

Reduced blood
pressure
(indicates less stress)

Advanced and therefore clairvoyant seers, observed that certain sounds had effects on the chakras . They recognised that each chakra was associated with a particular sound which caused it to spin, stirring some aspect of our higher consciousness.

How this works can be explained by modern physics. When a particular sound vibration resonates at the same frequency as the chakra, it causes the chakra to spin.

WHAT THE YOGIS SAY

According to the doctrine upon which mantra meditation is based, the primary manifestation of the Ultimate Reality takes place through the agency of a subtle vibration, which in Sanskrit is called *Sabda*, meaning sound. The world is not only created, but maintained by this sound, which differentiates into innumerable forms of vibration which underlie the phenomenal world.

It is necessary first to understand how all the phenomena of nature can be ultimately based on **vibration** or peculiar expressions of energy. First, let us take the material side of these phenomena. Physical matter has been found by science to consist of atoms and molecules which in their turn are the result of different combinations of still smaller particles like electrons, etc.

Even though matter seems solid to us, in actual fact, the ultimate nature of matter is energy. This has been proven by Einstein's Theory of Relativity which shows that **matter and energy are not two different entities but one and the same,** the relation between the two being given by the well known equation : $E = MC^2$, where E equals energy, M equals Mass or Matter, C equals velocity of light.

Not only is matter an expression of energy, but the perception of material phenomena depends upon vibrations of various kinds. Vibrations of different kinds striking the organs of sensation, produce the five kinds of sensations. The familiar world of light, sound, etc., is thus based on vibrations.

It is a logical doctrine that the foundation of the whole manifested world consisting of innumerable occurrences is really a tremendously complex and vast aggregate of vibrations of various kinds and degrees.

According to the yogis, all these infinitely complex vibrations are the expressions of a **single vibration**, which is regarded as the ultimate reality. It is the sound we use for the mantra meditation technique in this book. It is the basic vibration of the universe and life and has such a potent effect on unfolding our higher consciousness.

THE MANTRAS WHICH STIMULATE THE CHAKRAS

There are seven major chakras or energy centres along the spine. Each one is associated with a specific sound and if this sound is repeated as in mantra meditation, it will stimulate and activate that particular seat.

CHAKRA 1 - THE ROOT CHAKRA

Sound - Ooo as in home.

Location - The base of the spine.

Function - Responds to any issues concerning **survival** - eating, sleeping, exercising, convalescence, making a living.

If there is some damage to this chakra, we find ourselves repeatedly coping with threats to our survival. This keeps us from focusing on other things such as learning, creativity or relationships.

CHAKRA 2 - THE SEAT OF LIFE

Sound - U as in rule.

Location - Lower abdomen, centred between the navel and the genitals.

Function - **Sexuality, emotions, sensation, pleasure, movement** and **nurturance.**

If this chakra is in poor condition, we become dull, lifeless, out of touch, impassive, with no interest in sexuality.

CHAKRA 3 - THE POWER OF LIFE

Sound - Ah as in father.

Location - At the solar plexus (about 5cm above the navel).

Function - Gives us **vitality** and **will-power.** If this chakra is flawed, we may feel tired, afraid, quiet or withdrawn. There is fear of taking risks, confronting people or issues and taking charge. We also tend to be too serious and not laugh enough.

CHAKRA 4 - THE HEART CHAKRA

Sound - Ay is in play.

Location - Over the heart.

Function - Grants us **the capacity to give and receive love, as well as to "love" ourselves.**

If this chakra is not working, we lose our capacity to give and receive love, and suffer from poor self-esteem.

CHAKRA 5 - THE THROAT CHAKRA

Sound - Ee as in free.

Location - Bottom of the neck.

Function - **Communication** and **creativity.**

If this chakra is damaged, there is fear of expressing oneself, or excessive shyness.

CHAKRA 6 - THE VISION CHAKRA (THE THIRD EYE)

Sound - Mm as in hum.

Location - Level of the forehead, in between the eyebrows.

Function - This is the centre of **visual, psychic** and **intuitive** perceptions.

If this chakra is impaired we may experience eye trouble, headaches or bad dreams.

It is mainly this chakra which is stimulated when we use the mantra meditation technique in this book, since this energy centre is concerned with higher consciousness and intuition.

CHAKRA 7 - THE CROWN

Sound - Ng as in sing.

Location - Crown of the head.

Function - This chakra is the gateway to **Cosmic Consciousness**, the ultimate goal of meditation. We will not concern ourselves with this seat, since it is only for very advanced meditators and personal supervision is essential.

THE BODY OF LIGHT

In summary, the chakras located along the spine are the **anatomical mechanism** for higher consciousness, while the stimulation of the chakras by meditation is the **physiological mechanism**.

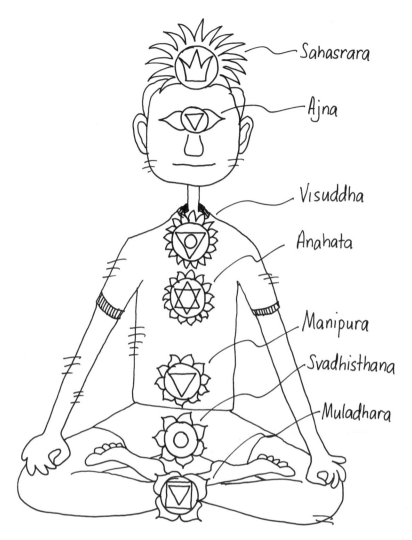

Sahasrara

Ajna

Visuddha

Anahata

Manipura

Svadhisthana

Muladhara

HOW TO CORRECT YOUR CHAKRA PROBLEMS

If you feel you have any problems with any of your chakras, just spend a few minutes each day, when breathing out, chanting aloud the sound associated with the problem seat. Let your sound be full bodied and resonant. At the same time, visualise the location of the chakra.

If you have a problem with two chakras you may use one sound while breathing in and another sound while breathing out. I don't advise you work on more than two chakras at a time. When you have made sufficient improvement then you may work on the other problem chakras.

HIGHLIGHTS

- The two meditation techniques presented in this chapter are the **most effective** for stress release. They are also very **simple**.

- The **Tranquil Breath Meditation Technique** works by **distracting the mind** from its habitual thinking and allows it to get used to living in the present (the here and now).

- The **Breath** is an ideal tool for meditation since it is a **natural** function. It provides an **anchor** for the mind and acts as a **marker-buoy**, letting us know when the mind is wandering away.

- The **Mantra Meditation Technique** works by the **sound** of the mantra having a **vibratory stimulating effect** on the higher consciousness centre — the **pineal gland chakra** in the hypothalamus area of the brain. This is also the area which deals with **stress**.

- If you have any **specific problems**, you may "treat" the **offending chakra** by repeating the associating mantra sound for a few minutes while breathing out. Visualise the location of the chakra. If you have two problem chakras, use one sound for inhaling and another sound for exhaling. Do not work on more than two problem energy centres at the same time.

CHAPTER 7

YOUR MEDITATION SESSIONS

Oh! Dreadful is the check — intense the agony
When the ear begins to hear, and the eye begins to see;
When the pulse begins to throb, and the brain to think again;
When the soul to feel the flesh, and the flesh to feel the chain.

Emily Brontë, *The Prisoner*

Our lives need order. This is not just cleaning out cupboards or restructuring the office inventory, but an **order** inspired by contacts with higher levels of awareness. It is an order that stops us dissipating our energies. It makes us concentrate our forces and enables us to break through our sense-bound realities.

We have terms for it: a focused life, clarity of vision, a tranquil outlook.

Mental conditioning makes us impose so many pre-requisites for happiness. Thus, we think people should have money, should be married, should have children and grandchildren, should live in big houses, should drive sleek cars, should travel regularly, should have lots of shopping money and so on, to be happy. It is all a product of unimaginative and conventional thinking, goaded by the pressure pumps of society. It is also a manifestation of a self-centred way of viewing life — we cannot imagine somebody being happy when he or she does not have what we have, and more. This is how we think when we are not guided by intuition and intelligence. This is how it is when we function from the lower levels of awareness.

The reality: It's not the state of your finances or your civil status or the size of your house that brings you happiness. A new house or another child will not save a crumbling marriage; a genuine change of attitude on both parties might. Unhappy people think a relationship is their panacea. Most are puzzled when the situation only worsens. Unhappy people tend to be difficult people who see or cause a lot of strife around them. They put tremendous stock in the new relationship, depending on its magic to solve the vague unease that has caused them feelings of isolation for so long. When it does not do the trick, they blame their partners or their careers or their environment. Hostile children who have had histories of conflicts with their parents often end up with difficult marriages.

The problem in all of the situations cited is one of attitude. The complication resides in the warring couple and the unhappy person and the hostile child. When they change, their lives change. When there is no harmony in your life, no external prizes will help — no trip to exotic cities, no Rolls Royce, no Special Other. You've got to change.

THE HARMONIOUS LIFE

We look out and think that, out there, is the secret to happiness. The recipe is much, much simpler. The well of harmony and joy resides in us, the key to it is in our hands. Those who acknowledge this are fortunate for they won't be losing time searching for answers in other people and in material things. They know that if only they raise the level of their consciousness, they will achieve the order that puts an end to strife and conflict.

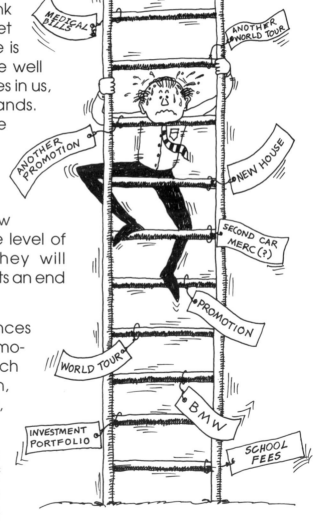

Personal circumstances are irrelevant — the harmonious life is the best life. Rich or poor, handsome or plain, tall or short, slim or stocky, it does not matter.

But our lives have been long stretches of busy years where we've been marooned at the level of restless thought. Our awareness has been bogged down by worry, tension and impatience.

The higher consciousness has therefore remained dormant for years. The Real Self has been pushed back, concealed by everyday masks we wear to achieve an endless list of desires. But it is there, like an heirloom, half-forgotten. All we need is to look deep and enjoy it once again.

Let us begin.

A FEW PRELIMINARY WORDS

1.   The main aim of our meditation sessions is stress release. Your goal is thought reduction, a calming of the mind. The beyond-thinking phase will happen in time. Just persevere and proceed at your own pace. You, too, will experience the rare moments of no-mind.

Beginners have been demoralised after listening to the wonderful tales of other meditators. In fact, even people who have been meditating for a bit are sometimes made to feel they are not doing things properly when they exchange notes with these meditators. Some people give the impression that peak experiences, moments of utter bliss and wonderful no-mind radiance happen to them with amazing regularity.

Just listen without judging. Then think of rolling all the amazing bits you've heard in an imaginary envelope and throwing this in the next dustbin. Avoid comparisons.

Every other thing in this world is a competition — who has brighter children, who has a lucrative profession, who made a killing on the property market. Don't allow meditation to be another contest. Don't be drawn to one. Make it your very private affair with secret joys to light your life.

IT'S NOT ANOTHER LADDER

2.   Meditation is your way out of stress. It is not another career, not another job, not another interest where you are expected to excel, compete and earn kudos. It is not another ladder to climb. You just might overdo things again if you treat meditation as another "field of endeavour" where you are supposed to succeed and be better than your peers. In assigning new goals to your meditative life, you run the risk of creating new tensions.

There are meditators who draw up elaborate schemes to meditate in expensive hill stations or exotic far-flung islands and get upset when their plans are thwarted. They end up bickering with those who threaten to stop them, claiming their quest for peace is being sabotaged. Where's the higher consciousness here, you ask. Good question. In their case, meditation takes a back seat to the glamour of doing it somewhere special. No different from competitive golfers who boast having conquered challenging courses. But in fairness to golfers; they don't claim having passports to enlightenment!

Promise yourself that you will not use meditation as another tool to compete and show off.

Now we can move on.

PREPARATIONS

When to meditate

For optimum results, you should meditate twice daily. Ideally, these sittings should be scheduled for early morning, before breakfast, and in the early evening, before your meal.

It is important not to meditate at least an hour after eating a light snack and four hours after eating a heavy meal. The body draws blood from the brain to assist in the digestion of food and this can reduce the effectiveness of the session.

Again, don't impose strict rules. The times suggested here may be ideal but may not suit your schedule, or your personal preferences. You may find that meditating during your noon break, before a light lunch, works for you — do it then.

Try to meditate daily but do it when you can. Pinning yourself to exact times would be ideal, but could be tricky especially if you live with other people. Being too rigid causes more stress so be adaptable. What happens if a friend drops in unexpectedly shortly before your meditation? What happens when your wife invites the neighbours for drinks before the evening meal? If your child is suddenly taken ill just as you are settling down to meditate, what do you do?

Meditation will have its way of making you adapt calmly to interruptions. Meditation will also work out a harmonious scheme where you will be able to fit your personal wishes and your perceived obligations.

But before learning this new proficiency, remember this: You have 24 hours in a day, just like everybody else. Somewhere there you will find time to meditate.

Duration of sitting

Fifteen minutes is the minimum time to achieve progress. Twenty minutes will produce optimum results.

Remember the need to be adaptable? There may be occasions when you will be pushed for time. When these occur, do as much as you possibly can, without getting flustered. A five-minute session is better than nothing. As long as you remember to be still and quiet some time during the day, you will feel better. In fact, ten very good minutes of stillness will benefit you more than twenty minutes where half your mind is bothered by thoughts of running late for an appointment or someone waiting.

An alarm clock might prove disturbing so, to check the time, you may half open your eyes when you feel you've done the allotted 15 minutes. But try not to worry about the time.

If you really wish to complete the full fifteen minutes without having to half-open your eyes to check how you're doing (surely this is a sign that your mind is beginning to wander?), you may use an alarm clock. However, give yourself a few extra minutes past the sitting's duration before making it ring. If you begin at 6:15, adjust the clock for 6:32. You don't want to be jolted at exactly 6:30. The sound at 6:32 should indicate to you that you have completed your session and may begin to resurface.

Resurfacing means sitting there for another minute or two with your eyes still closed. Enjoy the feeling of peace, clarity and energy. This period allows your brain to assimilate the benefits of meditation and makes for a smooth transition from your inner world to your outer one.

Where to meditate

You can meditate anywhere and as your level of awareness gets raised, you will be able to do it even in places buzzing with activity or blaring with noise. Experienced meditators can switch off in the middle of traffic jams.

However, in the beginning and while you are releasing a lot of superficial stress, it is best to meditate in a quiet place. This can be your bedroom, your study, your kitchen, even your garage. There's no mumbo-jumbo in meditation. You don't — you may, only if you wish to — need to turn off the lights or burn incense or play music.

It should be pointed out, though, that the good vibes produced by meditation create a feeling of calm and peace where the session is done. If you do it at a specific spot regularly, a build-up of positive vibes will make it a calming corner by itself. This is an added bonus that will increase the beneficial effects of your meditation sessions.

Prevent being disturbed. This is simple if you live alone. You can take the phone off the hook and, if you have a mobile phone, turn it off. More adept approaches will have to be made if you live with others or you have a family. Your companions, your spouse or your children will co-operate. The problem is usually one of perception; it is in our heads that they won't. We don't voice our requirements and get resentful when they barge in the room with some small attention-seeking gesture just as we are getting more relaxed. Tell them. Request them not to disturb you for the next 15, 20 minutes. Once your family members observe the changes in you, they will stop begrudging you the time you don't spend at their beck and call.

What would one give for a more relaxed, more tolerant, more caring and more enthusiastic spouse/parent/friend?

Let us now sit.

THE MEDITATION TECHNIQUE

This is a combination of the tranquil breathing and the mantra meditations presented in Chapter 6. Combining the two most effective stress-releasing techniques produces a very potent method.

You observe the flow of the breath, in and out, at the opening of the nostrils.

As we exhale, we silently repeat the mantra, **AUM.**

The breath is the anchor. It allows us to rest the mind there, in the here and now. The breath also becomes a buoy or marker since it lets us know when the mind begins moving away and wandering.

When the mind starts turning away from the breath, it is once more seeking happiness. The mind is always reaching out for it and it thinks it is out there, away from the breath.

The mind is therefore being distracted by the illusion of happiness. The well of happiness is in us and the breath will lead us to it. Every time the mind wanders off, gently lead it back to the breath.

Don't try to control it. The body has been breathing quite well without your help since you were born. It knows exactly what to do so let it do its job naturally. It's like watching waves at the beach. Waves come and go without any assistance from anyone. Natural things are best left alone. So don't interfere with the breath, just watch it as you would watch the waves.

You are a silent observer, just experiencing the breath. Keep your focus light. Observing is not concentrating. Just gently take hold of the breath and feel it.

If we give importance to the breath, it will be much easier to keep our attention on it and reduce intruding thoughts. We have always taken it for granted because it has always been there and we have had more important things to do.

When you are meditating, consider the breath as the most important thing in the world. It is!

THE MANTRA

The mantra we use in this meditation is considered by the ancient meditation masters to be the most potent. According to the yogis, it is the cosmic sound, or, if you like, the background sound of the universe. It is the sound of **AUM**, pronounced O as in home or AU as in auto.

This mantra affects the chakra which is responsible for the higher consciousness. It is situated in the area of the pineal gland, between the eyebrows. It is often called the "third eye" by mystics and occultists. The mantra produces the best effect for unfolding your full potential since it has the same resonant frequency as the pineal gland chakra.

The pineal gland lies in a particular area of the brain called the hypothalamus. The hypothalamus deals with stress.

When stress occurs, the hypothalamus discharges the cortico-trophin- releasing hormone (GRH) into the pituitary gland. This, in turn, secretes hormones into your bloodstream. Your adrenal

INTERNAL STRUCTURE OF THE BRAIN
SHOWING THE HYPOTHALAMUS

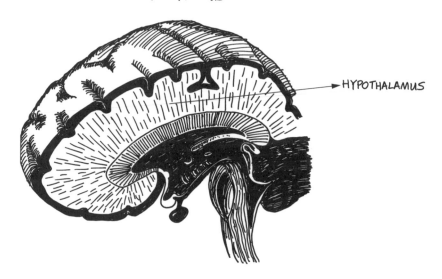

HYPOTHALAMUS

glands are thereby activated to produce more hormones resulting in increased pulse rate, increased rate of breathing and reduced metabolism. This is the 'fight or flight' mechanism we discussed in Chapter 1.

So while the hypothalamus is the primary centre where you feel stress, it is also the centre for releasing stress. You realise now why the mantra can be very potent.

SITTING

1. Wear comfortable clothes. Do you feel too cold? Too hot? See to it that you feel comfortable before you begin meditating.

2. Place the clock where you can see or reach it easily. If you want to use the alarm, remember to give yourself an extra couple of minutes before making it ring.

3. Take the phone off the hook if you are alone. If there are other people in the house, tell them please not to disturb you for the next 20 minutes.

4. If you're using a chair, choose a straight back one and support your back, without leaning against the chair. Rest your feet firmly on the ground.

    If you're using a cushion, make sure its height is right and it is firm. The correct way is to sit on the front half of the cushion so your crossed legs are on the floor in front of you. This tilts your pelvis forwards, making your spine straight. It is also very comfortable.

5. Your arms should hang loosely on either side of you with the hands on your lap, palms upwards, so that one gently rests on the other, thumbs touching at the tips.

6. Now close your eyes and just breathe easy. After a minute or two, your breathing will be relaxed and even. Only when the breath has become slow and steady should you begin meditating.

7. Locate the breath by paying attention to the entrance of the nostrils and begin observing the even flow of the breath, in and out.

8. Say, **AUM** when you exhale. About the first half of the exhaling should be **AU** and the last half, **Mmm.** If this complicates things in the beginning, just do the breathing in the morning and the mantra in the evening. If you can do only one session, then observe the breath. When you become more proficient at meditating, you might like to try doing the combination again.

9. The breath may be difficult to find and stay with in the beginning. Be patient. When thoughts arise, just simply, gently, return to observing the breath. Thoughts have been arising all day and they are not stopping for you while you meditate. But staying with the breath will reduce them drastically.

10. So focus lightly on the breath (the experience). The aim is to reduce the number of thoughts (the commentary), not to stop them altogether which is not possible at this time anyway.

Don't try to stop thoughts. Any attention you give them empowers them. Thoughts are part of the ego and the ego thrives on attention.

Returning the attention to the breath means the thoughts get no attention. The ego can't handle this and will gradually fade away, and with it, much of the constant mental chattering.

11. When the alarm goes, just quietly turn it off. You may be able to do this without having to open your eyes. Spend the next couple of minutes in the silence without having to watch the breath. At this point, you may wish to remind yourself of something you want to be rid of — your impatience, say — or something you want strengthened, like ties with people you love.

12. Slowly open your eyes and stretch. To maximise the benefits of your meditation, you can, if you have the time, stay seated in the same chair. If you can look out a window, observe the scene

quietly, whatever it is. Do this between sips of water. The calm that you will feel will make you look forward to the next sitting.

FOOD FOR THOUGHT

Remember the old Chinese proverb that speaks of a thousand mile journey beginning with a single step?

If you thought of a journey which took 1000 miles, you would probably never take it. But if you went anyway and just put your attention on one step at a time, the present, it becomes easy. You just concern yourself with the step you are taking now. One day, that step becomes the last. The journey of 1000 miles is completed but for you it has just been one step long.

Likewise, even though your tranquil breath meditation may be a thousand breaths long, it is really just one breath — the one you are breathing now.

ADOPT A RELAXED ATTITUDE

Stop wondering whether you are doing it properly or not. Just sit quietly and forget results. If you stay with the breath, you are doing the meditation technique correctly. It's that simple, so simple that some may doubt its efficacy. We are so conditioned to doing mental gymnastics that we think to release stress we must use a very sophisticated, very "learned" method. The ego does not like simplicity. It wants frills, fuss; it demands extravagance. All that need for frills is the root cause of stress.

The mind is transformed by utter simplicity — a few moments of stillness, watching the breath. The breath is, in itself, extremely tranquil, peaceful and soothing.

When you first start to meditate, you may experience an overwhelming onslaught of thoughts. Do not get intimidated.

This is natural because your mind is not used to being still. It fights your effort to be quiet. Don't fight back. Just keep on returning to the breath.

There may be occasions when you have a lot of worries on your mind. These worries may get more insistent when you meditate. This is natural and nothing to be concerned about. Don't think you are making a mistake. Just keep watching the breath. After your meditation, you will be calmer and your thinking, clearer. You will be able to handle your problems much better. It is the nervous fussing that makes worries seem monumental.

IF YOU ARE FEELING TENSE

If you are feeling very tense just before you meditate, you may find it hard to settle down both physically and mentally. I suggest you do a very simple yoga relaxation technique which only takes a couple of minutes and is very effective. Here's how to do it:

1. Lie on your back and tense the following areas of your body, one area at a time for about five seconds, and then let go — **face, eyes,** (close tightly), **jaw, neck, arms** (together) **and legs** (together). This is the best way to relax your body.

2. **Quickly scan the areas you have relaxed** to see if there is any tension left in any part of the body. If there is, just repeat the process for that area or areas.

3. Finally, repeat silently and slowly to yourself, "let go".

WHEN YOU ARE IN PAIN

A large component of pain comes from our emotional reaction to it. This can only occur if we allow our attention to dwell on the pain.

To stop pain interfering with your meditation, keep turning your attention to the breath. If you suffer from severe pain, the meditation will lessen its intensity.

The meditation technique I recommend is also very potent for alleviating the emotional trauma of disease. When the worries about your illness threaten to overwhelm you, do the meditation. You could do it even when you are bed-ridden. Watching the breath will release stress and leave your mind less cloudy. If you are undergoing treatment or are under medication, the meditation will make you more positive towards these and help in the healing process.

A COMMON TRAP

Most of us have very high stress levels so when we start to meditate, we release a lot of stress and feel much better. The contrast between your pre-meditative stressful life and your post-meditative relaxed life will be quite pronounced. It will appear that most of the benefits occur in the first week or two. After that, it may seem that nothing much happens.

This is not the case. During the first few weeks you will shed a lot of your superficial or **surface stress**. After that you will start to shed your deeper layer of **chronic stress** — stress you've had for many years and is deeply ingrained into your nervous system.

If you stop meditating after the first few weeks like some people do, you will **probably accumulate new stress** and be back where you were. In addition, you still have your deeper levels of stress. Also, remember that the benefits of meditation are **cumulative**, that is, the more you do, the more you benefit. It's like an athlete training every day for a big event. Every day he gets fitter. Each day's training adds up to produce a higher level of fitness.

KEEP IT UP

Because of the vital importance of meditation for stress release and happiness, it's extremely important that you are regular with your meditation. If you miss the odd one or two sessions a week, that's OK — but try not to miss any more.

As with exercise, you have to be regular to get maximum benefit.

Don't try to kid yourself that you haven't got the time since you have a lot of other things to do. Let's get our priorities right. The **number one priority in life is to live from our higher consciousness**, or if you like, unfold our full potential. The reason for this is that it leads to everything else — happiness, a stress-free life, increased health and vitality levels and success. **This is not being selfish.** You can help people far more and get on with people far better when you are happier, less-stressed and have more energy.

When you understand the value of something, you will **find time** for it. If necessary, go to bed a little earlier so you can get up a little earlier. Try to simplify your life, so you have time for the more important things in life.

The best way to be regular with meditation is to **realise its importance**. Realise it's the **only** way to happiness because it's the only way to bring out our higher consciousness.

TECHNIQUE SUMMARY

Preparation

- **Best time** — twice a day — before breakfast and before evening meal.
- **Duration** — 15 to 20 minutes.
- **Choose a quiet place** — wherever there are no distractions.

Posture

- **Sit upright** — push lower back slightly forwards and slightly lower chin.

The Technique

- **Observe the flow of the breath**. . . in. . . and. . . out. . . at the opening of the nostrils. When you pause in between breaths, keep your attention there.
- **While exhaling** — silently repeat the mantra **AUM** slowly. Don't try to concentrate on the mantra. Just repeat it.
- **After the session** — sit there with eyes closed for a couple of minutes. Enjoy the feeling of peace, clarity and energy.

Useful hints

- Breathe normally. Don't try to control the breath.
- Don't use any effort. Lightly focus on the breath.
- When thoughts arise, just gently return to the breath.
- Don't worry how well you are doing. Forget results!

CHAPTER 8

UNFOLDING
THE HIGHER CONSCIOUSNESS

A meditation master was building a retreat himself since he could not afford to employ tradesmen. It was a simple structure, no bigger than a hut, but made of bricks. One of his students happened by as he was completing the job. The young man commented that one of the walls, a total of 1,000 bricks, had two bricks sticking out a little.

The master smiled. "I hope," he said, "you've also noticed the 998 bricks which are all in line."

While steadily sloughing off the layers of stress left by years of unresolved business, regular meditation allows the advance of the higher consciousness into the mind. Since the very nature of the higher consciousness is bliss, intuition, deep feelings, loving kindness and humour, your mind begins to take on these qualities.

Each time we meditate, we allow a little more of this blissful nature to permeate our minds. Each day, our life improves. It is like dyeing a cloth a different colour. Each time we put the material into the solution, it takes on a little more of the colour of the dye.

The process is not achievable by most of the personal development, motivation and self-help courses for which you pay a few hundred dollars. These make us a bit more aware about the world about us but do little to cause major shifts in our perception and feelings about ourselves and others. They are quick fixes, minus the drugs. They leave us on a high after listening to inspirational talks, but how long does the euphoria last? A few days, a few weeks? The talks move you but they may not really change your perspective because you remain rooted in the same level of consciousness. Let us use another analogy. It is like a horse tied to a wheel. The horse has a certain degree of latitude, but once it gets to the periphery of the circle, the rope stops it going any further.

Meditation breaks this rope, allowing the higher consciousness to re-discover depths of feelings that years of tension, endless desires and utter neglect have buried in layers of vague unease.

WHY MOST SELF-HELP COURSES FAIL

If we decide to use self-improvement techniques to make us happy and successful, we would individually have to improve all the aspects of life which lead to happiness and success. In practice, this is impossible to do.

Consider: how can one person concentrate on all the aspects of life he/she wishes to improve? People have their normal everyday lives to live, they have chores to do, at home and at work. Their minds are occupied enough. Lifting affirmations parrot-like from motivational tapes will not help. Merely saying to yourself, "I am calm and serene" or "I have a happy home" does not make you any calmer or your home any happier if the level of your consciousness has not been raised and your perspective has not shifted.

> **Meditation is the only way to unfold the True Self. All the other techniques work on the periphery of the same old conditioned self. If the mind is, in effect, working on the restrictions of the same old conditioned self without any concomitant expansion of horizons, how can there be any real improvement?**

The principles you learn from self-help programmes will really work for you if you complement them with regular meditation. It's like people who worship one day a week. The grace will permeate their lives only if they remember their faith on the other six days as well.

THE HIGHER CONSCIOUSNESS AT WORK

While we may meditate now primarily to release stress, the emergence of the higher consciousness will lead us to other things, like finer feelings which, in turn, will lead us to better states like happiness.

THE EFFECTS OF LIVING FROM OUR HIGHER CONSCIOUSNESS

HAPPINESS

SUCCESS ← HIGHER CONSCIOUSNESS → LOVE
via
MEDITATION

STRESS RELEASE

RECAPTURE THAT CHILDLIKE INNOCENCE

The best thing about children is their innocence. They are **simple, uncomplicated, spontaneous** and **happy.** In general, they have far more energy and are far happier than adults. You may say the reason is, they are much younger. So we have to examine the reason why we have allowed ourselves to get older, especially mentally. Ageing is largely **biological** and not so much chronological.

We age fast **physically** because of our lifestyle. Children do not eat so much rich fatty foods and drink alcohol. They run around all day getting exercise and fresh air. We age **mentally** because we worry too much and have lost the zest for life. We are too serious and have lost that playful attitude.

Why do we lose these childlike qualities? It is largely a result of **conditioning.** We are expected to become serious and "grow up" as we get older.

I maintain we can carry out our responsibilities and still enjoy the child-like qualities of being spontaneous, living in the present, not worrying, having a playful attitude and having a zest for life. But how do we do it?

When stress is released from the mind, you will **worry less** and recapture an enthusiasm for life. The emergence of your higher consciousness will make you more spontaneous and live more in the present. This is because it operates on the **intuition level** which is **timeless**, that is, instant or spontaneous and totally in the present.

LOVE AND MEDITATION

Love occurs when you have complete respect and admiration for another person. It is the ultimate appreciation of a person.

Love can only occur when the **nervous system is free from stress** and you are living at least to some degree from your **higher consciousness**. Both these prerequisites are achieved by doing meditation. Love is one of the natural characteristics of the higher consciousness and occurs **naturally** and **spontaneously** when living from this state.

What we commonly refer to as "love" is really based on physical and mental attraction and often involves wanting to possess the other person. It is also conditional, that is, we will only "love" that person if they do what we want them to do.

In other words, I will only love you on my conditions. This is really emotional mood-making and is an ego-type relationship. As we see once again, living from our ego level of consciousness causes suffering and causes us to miss out on the "**real thing**".

Real love is totally **unconditional**. If the other person doesn't love you, it should make no difference to how you feel. By the same token there should be no hurt because you are not supposed to be expecting anything — there are no conditions attached. In the beautiful words of the poet Kahlil Gibran:

"Love gives naught but itself and takes naught from itself:
Love possesses not nor would it be possessed;
For love is sufficient unto love;
And think not you can direct the course of love, for love,
If it finds you worthy, directs your course."

By releasing stress and unfolding our higher consciousness, meditation allows love to occur naturally, effortlessly and unconditionally.

RELATIONSHIPS

Men and women live together for most of their lives and yet, often, they remain total strangers. They talk to each other, do things together, make love and bring up children and yet they don't *really* know each other. This remarkable situation has been going on for thousands of years. To make matters worse, there is frequently conflict between the two. Why is this? Man and woman are relating to each other on a **superficial level.** It is this level which brings the opposite sexes together, but, once together, the **opposite causes conflict.**

The male and female natures are fundamentally different and unless there is a deep awareness and acceptance of this, problems arise. The woman accuses the man of not caring enough, not communicating enough. The man accuses the woman of not understanding his ambitions, his dreams. Conflict replaces the initial attraction.

Whether making love or fighting, the relationship is on the same superficial, physical level. There is no relationship at a deep level.

What is the solution to this age-old problem? We need to be aware that our partners' "natures" are different; we should cultivate **a caring, understanding attitude** to this difference. Instead of conflict we will then realise that the male and female natures **complement** each other, producing harmony and balance. We have to develop this awareness and caring understanding.

Counselling can help to a point, but the only effective way is meditation. It produces a **change** in our nature at a very **deep level**. This change allows you to understand the other person, and with understanding, **conflicts are resolved** with ease, or disappear.

At least one of the partners needs to meditate — preferably both. If we don't, we are stuck with the unsatisfactory situation which exists today.

WHEN FEELINGS GET BLUNTED

A lot of relationships break down due to one or both people in the union suffering from stress. Tension prevents us from acting intelligently and with tenderness towards the other person. Anxiety blunts our feelings. We overreact to whatever is causing us unease, and the excessive attention we put on it distracts us from the association. Relationship breakdowns also occur due to a lack of calm awareness of the other person or lack of sensitivity towards each other.

Communication occurs on other levels besides direct speech such as body language, nuances of expression and the way we speak. So we need to read between the lines — to hear what the other person is really trying to tell us. To pick all this up we need a calm, aware mind.

Meditation produces a calmness which enriches and enhances a relationship. Instead of conflict, it will be enjoyable and make us grow.

Much of the conflict that arises in a relationship is caused by perceived intrusions into each other's "space". This is not limited to our things spilling onto our companion's share of a desk or a room or a house, but includes the more important issue of individual privacy. The ego is so strong that it doesn't just want to direct us; it tries its best to control other people as well. This generates much hostility.

Regular meditation sharpens our ability to see the limits of our privileged roles in the lives of those we love. We realise that we do not own our companions; we don't even try to claim possession. We accept, without resentment, the fact that there are times when their likes/hobbies/opinions may differ from ours. We respect their occasional need to be left alone. More importantly, we stop trying to change them into the people we want them to be, namely, like us.

Stressed individuals are forever projecting their unease on others. The situation makes for very uncomfortable and edgy relationships.

TO LIVE IN THE PRESENT

As your higher consciousness unfolds, you will begin to live in the present. The higher consciousness exists **outside of time**, which, of course, is the present.

Time is really an **illusion**, conceived of by the ordinary mind. The past and the future don't really exist, except in our minds. The past is dead so why dig up a corpse? The future is a hypothetical concept. The past and future have no basis in reality. **The only reality is the present.** At first this point may not seem important, but, on further analysis, it has very significant implications. For example, let's take a look at one of the biggest scourges of mankind — **worry**. As well as being unpleasant, it has probably been responsible for more sickness and premature ageing than any other single factor. It is extremely destructive to the nervous system and the immune system, both of which are essential for health.

Let's analyse the nature of worry. Worry is what might happen in the future. Now, if you are rooted in the present, where's the worry? It simply cannot exist if you are in the here and now.

Of course, it is right to plan for the future but planning is different from worrying. Planning gives a semblance of order in your life, but flexibility is important here. It's the fussing, the repeated questions of *What if?* and the fidgeting about "results" that cause harm on the nerves.

The higher consciousness stops you fidgeting. It makes you cultivate spiritual poise.

FOCUS ON THE CAUSE, NOT THE RESULTS YOU WANT

We make the mistake of putting our attention on the effects we want without giving attention to the **cause** of those effects.

We have given our attention to the periphery of life instead of going to the centre — the core of our being. It's like the doctor who prescribes drugs for a certain health condition. Drugs often only treat the symptoms (effects). For a genuine cure, we have to give attention to the cause of the problem. In most cases, we have to raise our health level. An increased vitality level activates the body's own healing forces and boosts our immunity.

Similarly, by raising our level of consciousness by meditation, all aspects of our life improve. We become calmer, more concentrated, and more productive. We achieve our goals and have improved social relationships.

THINGS CHANGE FOR THE BETTER

When you begin to meditate, the Universal Intelligence will start to assist you in all aspects of your life. This happens because your higher consciousness has connections with the Universal Intelligence or the Universal Consciousness. As your higher consciousness develops through meditation, you start tapping into this cosmic intelligence. It expresses itself on an individual level by what we know as *intuition*. It surpasses the slow fallible thinking process of our normal daily consciousness.

Most of us struggle with things we want, whether it be a good job, a lot of money, a happy relationship and so on. Often we fail to achieve our goals because our minds are not as calm, as clear and as energetic as they should be. We are functioning from a low and sluggish level of awareness.

The reverse happens when the higher consciousness is working. Our thoughts become like magnets, attracting what we want. Goals stop seeming unreachable. We become confident and comfortable and things start feeling easier. The adage "life wasn't meant to be easy" applies to those who persist in living from their normal daily level of consciousness.

As the higher consciousness unfolds, our ego diminishes and with it all the problems our ego creates. Much of our suffering comes from living on the ego level. We no longer need to feed our ego, since we start to live from a much happier level — the higher consciousness, which by its very nature is bliss. So we become happier and life becomes easier.

Keep in mind the above process. It is a **gradual, subtle** progression. If we are regular with our meditation, as time proceeds, our higher consciousness increasingly infuses into our mind. It is most rewarding and comforting to realise that as you gradually replace the ego through meditation you are dealing with the root of your problems and inexorably tapping your higher consciousness.

TRUE SUCCESS IS DEVELOPMENT OF THE SELF

When we talk of success, we are usually referring to success in the outside world — business, money, goals, career, relationships, etc. But true success is really the **development of the Self.** This is not just a vague philosophical point — it is extremely practical. To start with, success in the external world will not make you happy. It may give temporary excitement, but that soon fades away and you are back to the same mental state you were in before. This is why people get restless, wondering, what next?

The old expression — "**You live in your mind**", is quite true. Happiness is a product of **how you feel inside**, not something external to you.

Secondly, success in the different aspects of the outside world is dependent on developing your inner world. It's the old principle of the **outer reflects the inner.** For example, if you are tired, feeling low and not relaxed, your inside world is not right and you have very little chance of succeeding in the outside world. How can you think clearly, plan effectively or have the energy

to do what you need to do if you are feeling sluggish or indifferent? It's like trying to make a machine productive when it is faulty. It simply can't be done.

"COINCIDENCES"

One of the things you will notice happening after you start meditating is that many "**coincidences**" will unfold. Here I mean far more than the laws of chance would normally allow. In other words, what you think about or require, will start evolving **automatically** for you. Again, this is due to the Universal Intelligence now working and causing your mind to act like a magnet, attracting whatever you think about. You will find things occurring at just the **right time** when you require them.

In my own life, I experience these convenient "**coincidences**" all the time. I find I ring people up and request something and things have "just fallen into line" to make my request possible. If this transpired once or twice it could be put down to coincidence, but it happens repeatedly. Something is obviously working for me. When this started, I wasn't taken aback since I knew it to be one of the effects of meditation. It makes life much easier and much less of a struggle.

If I may give you a personal example. Several of my patients had been recommending a newly published title — "The Celestine Prophecy". I rang the library to order a copy and they told me it was so popular it would be months before I would get it. The very next day a friend came to my house and gave me a book — you can guess which one. It had been one of his birthday presents. Because he would never read this sort of work in a million years, he gave it to me. The book was obviously meant for me.

YOUR CONCENTRATION POWERS WILL GREATLY IMPROVE

The practice of focusing your mind during the meditation period, will develop your ability to concentrate in **everyday** life. Normally, when we wish to focus our mind on a particular subject, distracting thoughts intrude. The same thing often occurs when we are reading, studying or even socialising. After meditation, the depth and span of your concentration will be much greater. This means you will get more satisfaction and be more successful in your day to day life.

One of the major factors in achieving your **goals** and being **successful,** is the ability to concentrate.

CREATIVE INTELLIGENCE

The higher consciousness enables us to cultivate the rewarding and joyful combination of intelligence and creativity. It makes us apply *creative intelligence* to projects we undertake, making each one doubly interesting.

Intelligence may be the meat, but creativity is certainly the sauce: it gives flavour to our intelligence. A creative mind finds new ways to have a more productive and enjoyable life; it does not just imitate or mimic somebody else's life. Haven't you noticed that successful designers are content wearing jeans or very severe outfits while their fashion victims strut about, wearing the latest fad, all of them looking alike?

You don't have to be an artist, a designer or an author. When the higher consciousness is at work, you become more responsive to life. You see depths you've ignored before and you respond to them accordingly. You see more humour in situations. You stop being too literal; you are able to read between lines. Creativity makes you see another person's point of view more sharply and this leads to more understanding and tolerance.

Intelligence and creativity are *synergistic.* They enhance each other. Increased intelligence allows us more scope to display our creativity. Increased creativity also gives us room to demonstrate our intelligence.

When we apply creative intelligence to any action, that action becomes extremely satisfying. As an example, we may wish to earn more. If we apply our intelligence to further this wish, we can achieve our goal. However, if we apply creativity to the task, life can become far more interesting as we explore hitherto unrecognised paths to prosperity.

A creative approach to a project makes it take on additional meaning. For the most part, the tedium of work and revision needed to complete anything is lessened. You become totally involved in it so time is not wasted on worries about deadlines and results. You commit less mistakes and complete the job faster.

People working from low levels of consciousness mistake their anxiety and worries for involvement. They think it's their "involvement" that harasses them and causes fatigue. People who generate so much stress in themselves and experience numerous panic situations think they are "too involved" with the process of living. Well, they aren't. They are actually half-alive — half of them is frozen by fear.

Creative intelligence liberates us from fear. Our intelligence and our creativity show us that if we apply the right actions, we need not fear for the ultimate results.

Self-help courses, mood music and motivational tapes can tell you about creative intelligence but only regular meditation can tap it. Only meditation can make the higher consciousness emerge and do countless wonders.

HIGHLIGHTS

- Meditation produces **true happiness** and **real success.** It will dramatically improve the **quality of your life** and make you **successful** in all areas of life — career, business and social relationships, etc.

- Meditation puts you more in **tune with nature** by bringing out your Real Self or higher consciousness. This will make you feel more centred and at peace with self and others. It will also cause you to live more in **harmony with nature** by desiring a **simpler lifestyle** and **more natural things.**

- Meditation will gradually unfold more of your full potential, resulting in **self-improvement**. Meditation allows your full potential to express itself by **releasing stress** and **unfolding your higher consciousness**.

- The only way to become **truly happy** is by raising your level of consciousness. This is because the very nature of the higher consciousness is **bliss**. The only way to achieve this is by meditation. This is real happiness, since it is **unconditional**. It does not depend on external circumstances, and is **permanent**.

- What we commonly refer to as happiness is really **excitement** of the senses. This is **temporary** and is usually followed by a "low". In between the rare and brief excitement periods we are generally restless. **Wealth** does not produce happiness, since you are still living from the **same** low level of consciousness, and this by its nature, is the **unhappy** consciousness level.

- **True Success** is the **development of the Self**, since success in the external world depends upon this, and in any case, success in the external world will not make you happy unless your inner self is developed.

- Meditation helps you to become successful by causing the **Universal Intelligence** to start working for you, since the higher consciousness is connected to it. It expresses itself as **intuition** and is 100% accurate, instant and effortless. Your thoughts will become like a **magnet**, attracting what you want and allowing you to achieve your goals easily and effortlessly.

- Meditation greatly **enriches our life** by increasing our intelligence and creativity. This enables us to utilise a very powerful and rewarding force — **creative intelligence.**

- Meditation **helps relationships** by **releasing stress** and giving us a **calm aware mind,** allowing us to know what the other person is really trying to tell us. Instead of conflict, relationships become **enjoyable** and contribute to our **growth.**

- **Real Love** can only occur when the nervous system is free from stress and you are living at least to some degree from your higher consciousness. With meditation, love occurs **naturally, spontaneously** and **unconditionally.**

CONCLUSION

A Useful List For Reflection

I have no doubt that when you're feeling bouyant about life, you wish to share your happy secret. Everyone who experiences the well-being brought on by meditation desires to create a snow ball effect. You want your parents, your spouse, your children and your friends to realise — the way you have — the benefits of meditation.

You're probably thinking: If they change the way I'm changing now, all problems will disappear and life will be perfect! It's the fever of the converted.

Our motivations may be well-intentioned but the noblest of intentions are lost on people who have not invited us to share their space. Our intrusions will only provoke antipathy.

Things happen in their own time. The people you're trying to convince will meditate once they see the need to do it. Nobody should push them into anything. You started meditating when you were ready for it. Allow others to go through the same learning pattern. They have a right to it.

Perhaps you feel enlightened. If you are, then you'll see that you should not initiate enlightenment games. Don't broadcast your no-mind episodes. Treat your peak experiences with respect — don't blow them on one-upmanship dramas.

Far better if you concentrate the energies gained from meditation in pursuing the interests and activities that, for some excuse — *there was always an excuse not to do things in the past* — you've pushed back into some neglected corner of your mind.

I have been asked, time and again: What happens after one becomes stress-free? After one has meditated, what next?

For a start, you can include the following in your reflections:

•**Organise your life.** Put your house and finances in order.

Start with your desk, your room, your medicine cabinet. Begin with your wardrobe, your kitchen shelves, your storeroom. Throw out what you don't need, what you haven't used for a year, what you've been saving for the past five years thinking it may one day be useful. Less clutter makes for a clearer mind.

•**Review your finances.** Exercise initiative and independence. Do your sums. Worrying is often the result of not knowing exactly where you stand. Make your own decisions about whether you have overextended yourself. Or whether it's time to give up an unprofitable venture. Or whether it's ripe to begin a new project. Or whether you should be rewarding yourself.

The cosmetic changes that occasional 'spring-cleaning' achieve are fine up to a point. Real changes will happen only when your innermost thoughts are revised.

•**Reward yourself daily.** This doesn't necessarily mean another expense as most people think. It could be an afternoon nap, putting your feet up, luxuriating in the bath, reading a good book. It's time reserved for yourself.

•**Observe your surroundings.** Take walks. Notice trees, shrubs, bushes. Pay attention to the sounds about you — the wind in the trees, the trilling of birds, laughter. Notice colours.

•**Keep in touch.** Procrastination should be a thing of the past. You will now find the time to write that letter, send that postcard, compose that e-mail. Never be too busy for friendships.

•**Mean what you say.** Put an end to empty speeches. When you tell a friend, "*let's get together*," do something about it. Don't make another promise until you have fulfilled an earlier one.

•**Accept all situations, good or bad, as part of a learning curve.** Things happen for a reason. Illness is the body complaining of neglect, or abuse. A loss is a message: have we been taking things for granted?

•**Maintain a healthy perspective.** Wisdom is the reward for pain and conflict handled with grace. Attitude matters.

•**Exercise moderation.** A healthy balance between work and play creates a harmonious life.

•**Cultivate the habit of thankfulness.** There is always something to be grateful for each day, from a slant of sunlight on our arm to the highs of the projects in which we are presently involved. Be grateful for the time allotted us.

NOTES

NOTES

NOTES

NOTES